Middle School Math Solution

Course 2

Skills Practice

501 Grant St., Suite 1075
Pittsburgh, PA 15219
Phone 888.851.7094
Customer Service Phone 412.690.2444
Fax 412.690.2444

www.carnegielearning.com

Cover Design Anne Milliron

ISBN: 978-1-60972-887-8
Skills Practice

Printed in the United States of America
1 2 3 4 5 6 7 8 9 CC 21 20 19 18 17

Table of Contents

Module 1: Thinking Proportionally

Module 2: Operating with Signed Numbers

Module 3: Reasoning Algebraically

Module 4: Analyzing Populations and Probabilities

Module 5: Constructing and Measuring

Topic 1

Circles and Ratio

Name ______________________________ Date ______________

I. Identifying Parts of a Circle and Congruent Circles

A. Identify the parts of each circle.

1. Use the circle shown to answer each question.

a. Name the circle.

b. Identify a radius of the circle.

c. Identify a diameter of the circle.

d. Identify a different diameter of the circle.

2. Use the circle shown to answer each question.

a. Name the circle.

b. Identify a radius of the circle.

c. Identify a diameter of the circle.

d. Identify a different diameter of the circle.

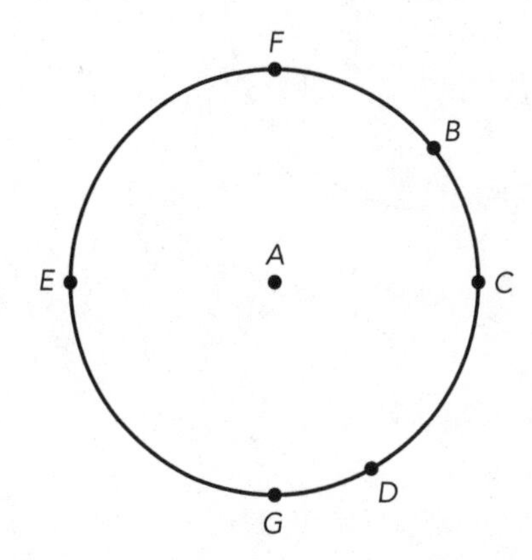

PAGE 2

3. Use the circle shown to answer each question.
   a. Name the circle.
   b. Identify a radius of the circle.
   c. Identify a diameter of the circle.
   d. Identify a different diameter of the circle.

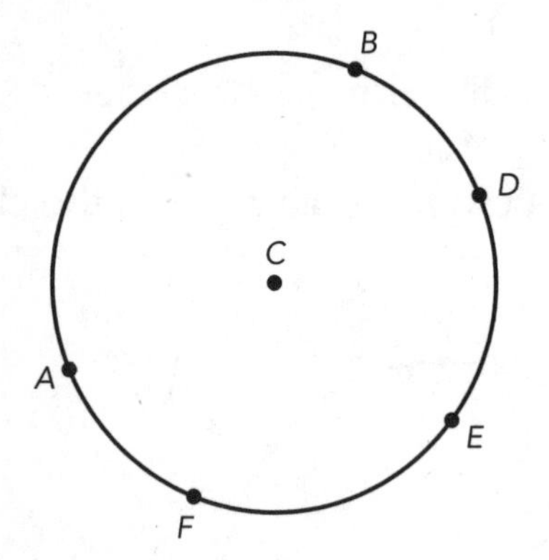

4. Use the circle shown to answer each question.
   a. Name the circle.
   b. Identify a radius of the circle.
   c. Identify a diameter of the circle.
   d. Identify a different diameter of the circle.

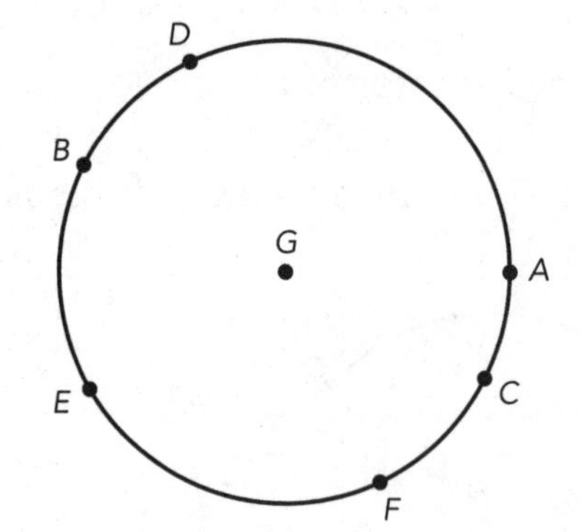

Name ______________________________ Date ______________

5. Use the circle shown to answer each question.

a. Name the circle.

b. Identify a radius of the circle.

c. Identify a diameter of the circle.

d. Identify a different diameter of the circle.

6. Use the circle shown to answer each question.

a. Name the circle.

b. Identify a radius of the circle.

c. Identify a diameter of the circle.

d. Identify a different diameter of the circle.

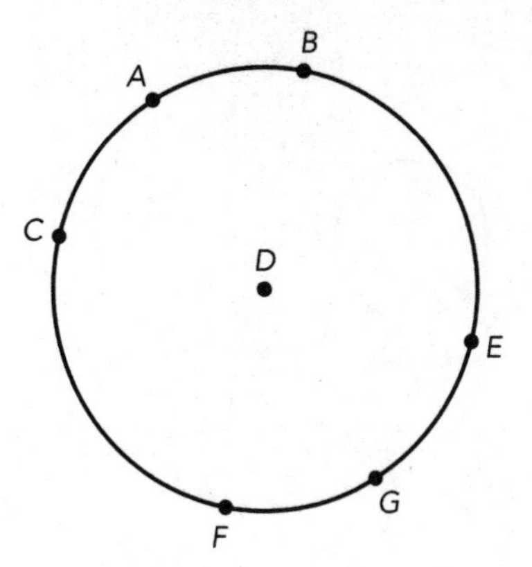

B. Determine whether the circles in each pair are congruent. The circles may not be drawn to scale.

1.

$r = 2$ cm

$d = 4$ cm

2.

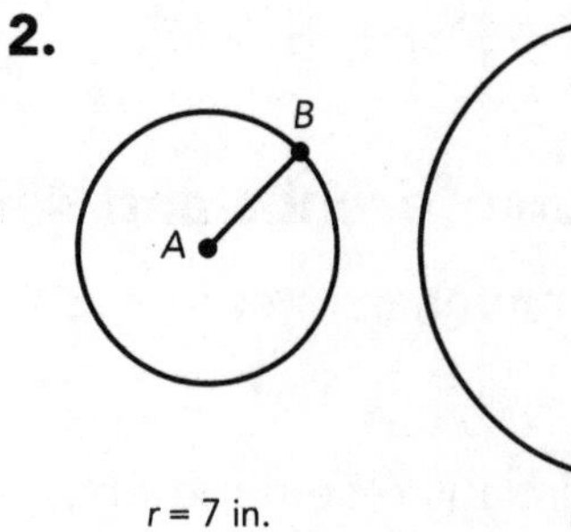

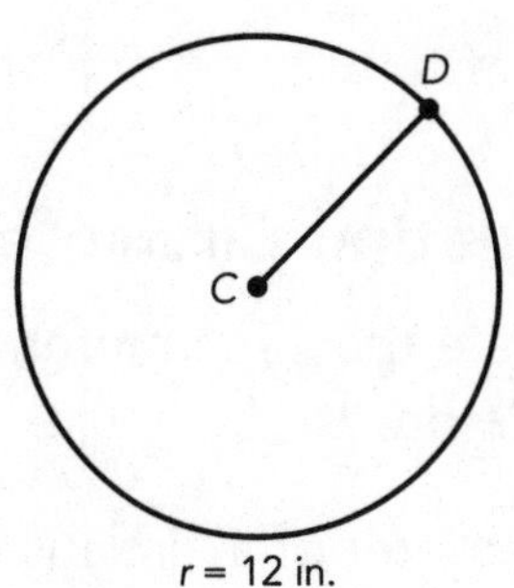

3.

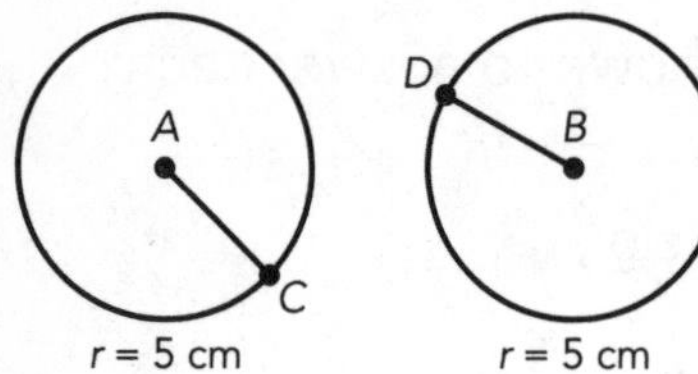

4.

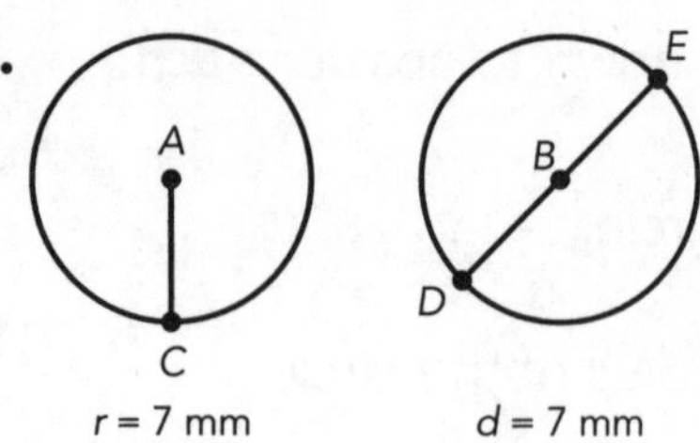

5.

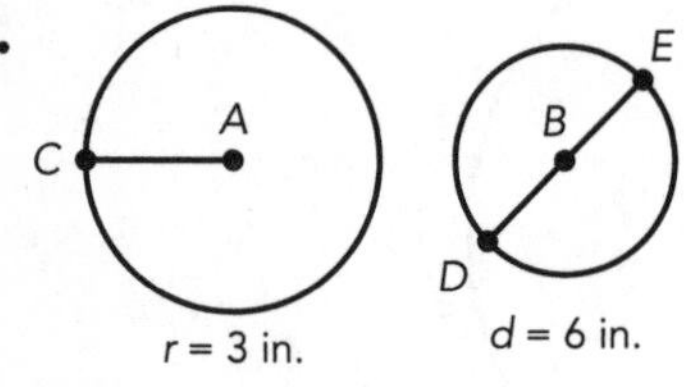

6.

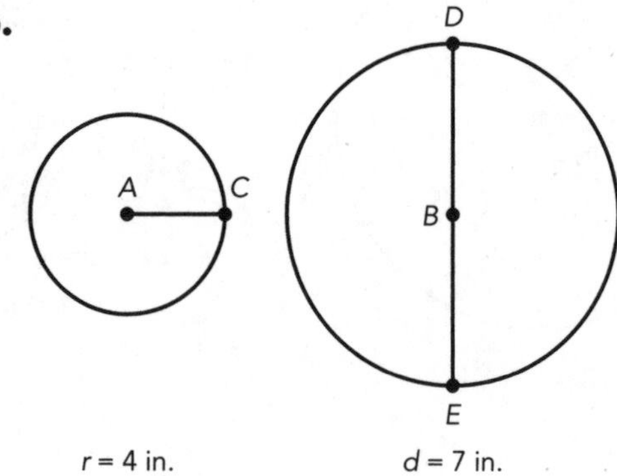

II. Calculating Circumference and Area of Circles

A. Calculate the circumference of each circle described. Use $\pi = 3.14$ and round to the nearest hundredth.

1. The diameter of a circle is 6 centimeters.

2. The radius of a circle is 8.2 centimeters.

Name ________________________________ Date ______________

3. The diameter of a circle is 7.5 inches.

4. The radius of a circle is 16.3 millimeters.

5. The diameter of a circle is 14 centimeters.

6. The radius of a circle is 2.1 inches.

B. Calculate each value using the formula for the circumference of a circle. Use $\pi = 3.14$ and round to the nearest hundredth.

1. The circumference of a circle is 56 centimeters. Calculate the diameter of the circle.

2. The circumference of a circle is 25.12 centimeters. Calculate the radius of the circle.

3. The circumference of a circle is 112.8 millimeters. Calculate the diameter of the circle.

4. The circumference of a circle is 49.6 inches. Calculate the radius of the circle.

5. The circumference of a circle is 47.73 millimeters. Calculate the diameter of the circle.

6. The circumference of a circle is 56.52 centimeters. Calculate the radius of the circle.

C. Calculate the area of each circle described. Use $\pi = 3.14$ and round to the nearest hundredth.

1. The diameter of a circle is 3 centimeters.

2. The radius of a circle is 2.5 centimeters.

3. The radius of a circle is 6 inches.

4. The diameter of a circle is 10 millimeters.

5. The diameter of a circle is 16 inches.

6. The radius of a circle is 4 centimeters.

III. Solving Problems with Circumference and Area

A. Solve each problem. Let $\pi = 3.14$. Round your answer to the nearest hundredth, if necessary.

1. You need to replace the cover for a light in your bathroom. The light cover is a circle. The circumference of the light cover is 43.96 inches. What are the radius and diameter of the light cover? What is the area of the light cover?

2. You order a pizza for dinner. The circumference of the pizza is 31.4 inches. What are the radius and diameter of the pizza? What is the area of the pizza?

Name ______________________________ Date ______________

3. You are responsible for setting the table for dinner. Each place setting has a circular dinner plate. The circumference of the dinner plate is 37.68 inches. What are the radius and diameter of the dinner plate? What is the area of the dinner plate?

4. You collect coins. One of your favorite coins is a silver-colored coin showing a man's portrait. The radius of the coin is 12 millimeters. What is the diameter of the coin? What is the circumference of the coin? What is the area of the coin?

5. You buy a new wheel for your bicycle. The diameter of the bicycle wheel is 22 inches. What is the radius of the bicycle wheel? What is the circumference of the bicycle wheel? What is the area of the bicycle wheel?

6. Your friend orders a new cover for his round swimming pool. The area of the pool cover is 200.96 square feet. What are the radius and diameter of the pool cover? What is the circumference of the pool cover?

B. Calculate the circumference or area to solve each problem. Let $\pi = 3.14$. Round your answer to the nearest hundredth, if necessary.

1. Jaleesa is buying a round backyard pool. The distance around the edge of the pool is 38 feet. Find the area that the pool will cover.

2. Belinda is digging a round flower garden in her backyard. She has 19 feet of rubber edging to place around the garden. What is the area of the new garden?

3. Carlos is spreading mulch in a circle on top of an area where he has planted some seeds. He has enough mulch to cover an area that is 12.5 square feet. How much rubber edging does Carlos need to encircle the mulch that will cover the seeds?

4. Jose is adding mulch to an existing round flower bed. The length of the rubber edging around the flower bed is 25.12 feet. What is the area that Jose needs to cover with mulch?

5. Eva is decorating for a birthday party. She would like to add a paper streamer around the edge of a round table. The table covers an area of 19.5 square feet. What is the minimum length of the paper streamer Eva needs?

6. Nami is adding a mosaic pattern to the top of a small round table. The distance around the edge of the table top is 4.7 feet. What is the area that Nami needs to cover with the mosaic pattern?

Topic 2

Fractional Rates

Name ________________________ Date ____________

I. Write Complex Rates and Unit Rates

A. Write each as a fractional rate.

1. A cell phone company mistakenly advertises that their data plan costs "0.02 cents" for every kilobyte of data.

2. Sue's Stop-n-Shop advertises that 12-ounce sodas are "0.99 cents" each.

3. A carnival game advertises "0.50 cents" for a ring toss.

4. At a yard sale, Enzo sees a sign that advertises "0.05 cents" per used book.

5. School Supplies R Us is having a back-to-school sale and advertises in the local paper that pencils are "0.88 cents" a pack.

6. Wesley's Wings and More advertises that wings are "0.25 cents" each on Monday nights.

7. A fast-food restaurant has a sign that water is "0.20 cents" for one cup.

8. A recycling center claims to give "0.04" cents for every aluminum can turned in.

B. Write each fractional rate as a unit rate.

1. $\frac{1}{2}$ cup for 3 batches

2. 5 miles in $1\frac{1}{2}$ hours

3. $\frac{2}{3}$ pound for every $\frac{1}{4}$ tablespoon

4. $2\frac{3}{4}$ gallons in $3\frac{2}{3}$ minutes

5. 6 pages every $\frac{1}{5}$ hour

6. $\frac{5}{6}$ yard for 4 dresses

II. Comparing Unit Rates

A. Answer each question by comparing unit rates.

1. Marcus can type 40 words in half a minute. Rhys can type 100 words in one and a half minutes. Which student can type at a greater rate of words per minute?

2. Yumi takes $\frac{5}{12}$ hour to complete 50 math problems. Eric is able to complete 48 math problems in $\frac{2}{5}$ hour. Which student can complete math problems at a greater rate of problems per hour?

3. Maggie's home computer downloads a 7 megabyte program in $\frac{5}{6}$ minute. Brooke's home computer takes $1\frac{1}{4}$ minutes to download a 9 megabyte program. Whose computer downloads at a greater rate of megabytes per minute?

4. Caitlin travels for $1\frac{1}{3}$ hours to visit a friend who lives $4\frac{1}{2}$ miles away. Martin travels $4\frac{1}{4}$ miles to visit a friend. It takes him $1\frac{1}{5}$ hours to get there. Who travels at a greater rate of miles per hour?

5. Beth drove 45 miles and used $3\frac{3}{4}$ gallons of gas. Martha drove 85 miles and used $5\frac{2}{3}$ gallons of gas. Which driver used fewer gallons of gas per mile?

6. Steve baked $5\frac{1}{2}$ batches of cookies in one and one half hours. Vondra baked $3\frac{1}{3}$ batches of cookies in $\frac{11}{12}$ hour. Which baker made cookies at a greater rate of batches per hour?

III. Solving Proportions Using Equivalent Ratios

A. Solve each problem by setting up and solving a proportion. Use equivalent ratios to solve the proportion.

1. The human body is often drawn using specific ratios. The average height of an adult is drawn using 7 head lengths (the height of the head is $\frac{1}{7}$ the total height). If a person in a painting is 63 centimeters tall, how tall is the person's head?

2. The Appalachian Trail is a 2,155-mile hiking trail in the Eastern United States. You plan to hike the section of the trail that is in New Jersey at a rate of 9 miles per day. If the hike will take you 8 days, what is the length of the trail in New Jersey?

Name ______________________________ Date ______________

3. The average person breathes 35 pounds of air per day. At this rate, how many pounds of air will the average person breathe in seven days?

4. You are on a hockey team. Your time on the ice is 12 minutes per game. A season is twenty games. How many minutes do you play during the season?

5. In an hour, a jogger burns about 4 calories per pound of body weight. How many calories will a jogger who weighs 151 pounds burn in an hour?

6. In the old British money system, 5 shillings was equal in value to 1 crown. Emily had 45 shillings. What was the value in crowns?

7. A movie package can be added to a customer's cable TV service for a cost of $8 per month. How much will the additional movie package cost for thirteen months?

8. Seventeen trees are saved for each ton of paper recycled. How many tons of paper will need to be recycled to save 51 trees?

9. There are 54 girls in a bowling league. There are two girls for every boy in the league. How many boys are in the league?

10. A typical home uses a total of seven kilowatts of electricity for each kilowatt of electricity used by the refrigerator. How much of a $70 electric bill is due to using the refrigerator, assuming that every kilowatt costs the same amount?

11. A jewelry store makes $5 profit for each $1 they spend on jewelry. A jewelry store owner made a profit of $95 on a necklace. What was the original cost of the necklace?

12. During long-distance races, a typical sled dog will run at a rate of approximately nine miles per hour. If a sled dog runs at this rate for 5 hours, how many miles could it run?

IV. Solving Proportions Using Means and Extremes

A. Solve each problem by setting up and solving a proportion. Set the product of the means and extremes equal to each other to solve the proportion.

1. The Arizona Cardinals won ten games out of sixteen of their games during the 2009 regular season. At this rate, how many games do they need to play to win 50 games?

2. The 18 wind turbines on Windy Hill are enough to meet the electrical needs of all 6 houses on Breezy Lane. How many wind turbines are needed to meet the electrical needs of 26 houses?

3. Between 1990 and 2000, the population of New York City increased at a rate of 32 people every four hours. By how many people would the population have increased in 63 hours?

4. A local survey determined that 4 out of every 10 Internet users have downloaded music at some point. At this rate, out of 60 Internet users, how many have downloaded music?

5. The string that produces the lowest tone on a piano vibrates 87 times in 3 seconds. How many times would this string vibrate in 12 seconds?

6. A 10-ounce package of animal cookies costs $2. What should a 35-ounce package cost, assuming the same cost per ounce?

7. On Mercury, you weigh 2 pounds for every 5 pounds you weigh on Earth. You weigh 135 pounds on Earth. How much do you weigh on Mercury?

8. After walking for 15 minutes, Zachary's treadmill displayed "120 calories burned". At this rate, how many calories will Zachary burn in 65 minutes?

Name ______________________________ Date ______________

9. A hybrid car uses 1 gallon of gasoline to drive 54 miles. How many gallons of gasoline would be used to travel 162 miles?

10. Nicholas owns a pet bearded dragon named Oscar, which is a type of lizard. It typically eats 51 crickets in 2 days. How many days has Nicholas fed Oscar if he has eaten 102 crickets?

11. In an hour, a downhill skier burns about 5 calories for each two pounds of body weight. How many calories does a 160-pound downhill skier burn in an hour?

12. You have started your own online business selling DVDs. You sell twenty-four DVDs per week online. How many DVDs do you sell in six weeks?

Topic 3

Proportionality

Name ______________________________ Date ______________

I. Identify the Constant of Proportionality

A. Answer each question.

1. Kim learned in her science class that every 2 minutes she spends in the shower, she uses 17 gallons of water. This rate is constant.

a. If Kim showers for 4 minutes, how many gallons of water will she use?

b. If Kim's sister used 119 gallons of water during her shower, how long was her sister's shower?

c. Identify the constant of proportionality for the time in minutes to the number of gallons.

d. Identify the constant of proportionality for the number of gallons used to the time in minutes.

2. A television time slot has 4 minutes of commercials for every 11 minutes of programming. This rate is constant.

a. If a television program is 88 minutes long, how many minutes of commercials should a viewer expect?

b. If there are 16 minutes of commercials, how long is the television program?

c. Identify the constant of proportionality for the minutes of commercials to the minutes of programming.

d. Identify the constant of proportionality for the minutes of programming to the minutes of commercials.

Name ______________________________ Date ______________

3. Each week, Best Foot Forward orders 8 boxes of socks for every 3 cases of shoes. This rate is constant.

a. If the store orders 96 boxes of socks one week, how many cases of shoes would it order?

b. This week, Best Foot Forward ordered 27 cases of shoes. How many boxes of socks did the store order?

c. Identify the constant of proportionality for the boxes of socks to the cases of shoes.

d. Identify the constant of proportionality for the cases of shoes to the boxes of socks.

4. In a survey that James conducted of the students in his school, he determined that 3 out of 8 students chose basketball as their favorite sport.

a. How many students choose basketball as their favorite sport if James surveys 240 students?

b. If 225 students chose basketball as their favorite sport, how many students did James survey?

c. Identify the constant of proportionality for the students who chose basketball to the students surveyed.

d. Identify the constant of proportionality for the students surveyed to the students who chose basketball.

5. Leron is weighing pennies for a science experiment. When he weighs 2 pennies, the weight is 5 grams.

a. How many pennies are on the scale if the weight measures 40 grams?

b. How much would 12 pennies weigh?

c. Identify the constant of proportionality for number of pennies to total weight.

d. Identify the constant of proportionality for total weight to number of pennies.

6. The Hidden Valley Cross Country Track Team is participating in a 3-day walk-a-thon to raise money for their favorite charity. They are asking each donor to pledge $18 for every 6 miles they walk.

a. How much money will the team raise if it walks 150 miles during the walk-a-thon?

b. How many miles does the team need to walk if they want to raise $615?

c. Identify the constant of proportionality for miles walked to money raised.

d. Identify the constant of proportionality for money raised to miles walked.

Name ______________________ Date ____________

II. Representing Proportional Relationships

A. Graph each proportional relationship. Then, write a proportion that shows the relationship between the two quantities (using the variables provided in the table) and the constant of proportionality.

1. Gerald is an event photographer. In his brochure he advertises that for every 4 posed pictures he takes of your event he will take 5 un-posed pictures. The table displays the possible number of posed pictures to the number of un-posed pictures.

Number of Posed Pictures	Number of Un-posed Pictures
posed pictures	un-posed pictures
p	u
16	20
24	30
32	40
36	45

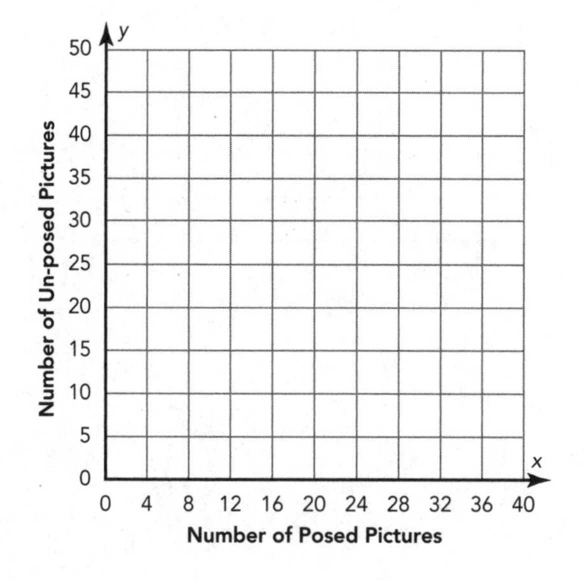

2. Tiffany is practicing her shots for basketball. For every 6 jump shots she practices, she practices 7 free throws. The table displays the possible number of free throws she practiced and the number of jump shots she practiced.

Number of Free Throws	Number of Jump Shots
free throws	jump shots
f	j
14	12
35	30
49	42
70	60

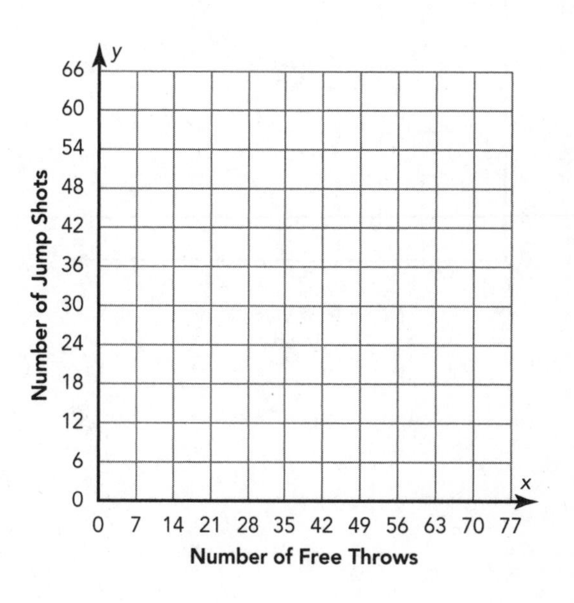

3. Howard is making necklaces out of glass beads. For every 3 red beads he uses, he uses 7 blue beads. The table displays the possible number of blue beads used and the number of red beads used.

Number of Blue Beads Used	Number of Red Beads Used
blue beads	red beads
b	r
28	12
42	18
56	24
63	27

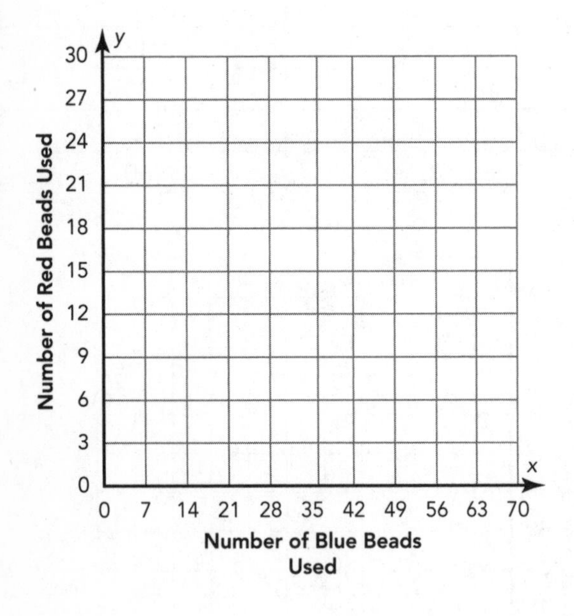

4. Allison is weighing money on a scale. She finds that 1 nickel weighs 5 grams. The table displays the possible number of nickels weighed and their weight in grams.

Number of Nickels	Weight in Grams
nickels	grams
n	g
2	10
6	30
7	35
9	45

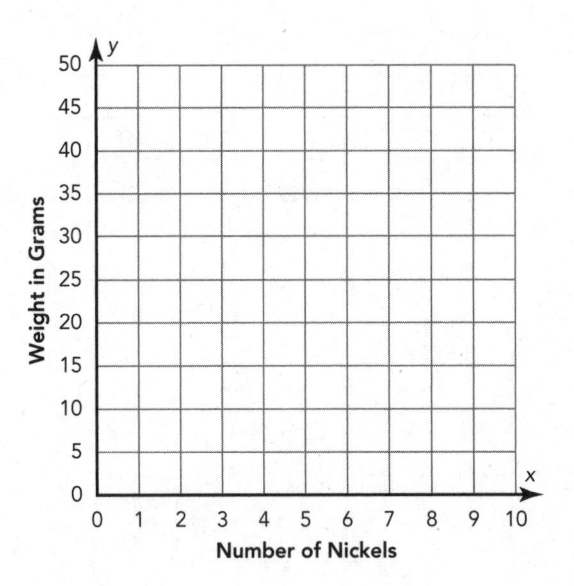

Name ______________________________ Date ______________

5. Sam is ordering reams of paper for his company using a website. He finds that every 3 reams of computer paper weigh 16 pounds. The table displays the possible number of reams of paper and the weight in pounds for each shipment.

Number of Reams of paper	Weight in Pounds
reams	**weight**
r	p
9	48
15	80
24	128
27	144

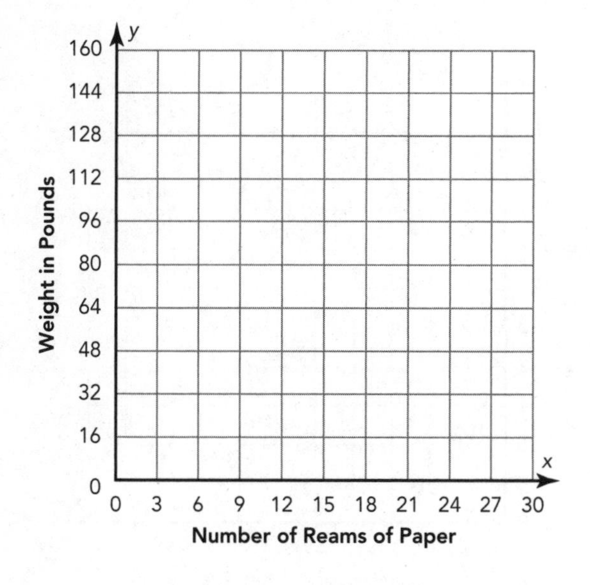

6. Nicholas takes his new puppy outside to get exercise every evening. For every 19 minutes Nicholas and his puppy walk, they play fetch for 5 minutes. The table displays the possible number of minutes Nicholas and his puppy walk and the number of minutes they play fetch.

Minutes Spent Playing Fetch	Minutes Spent Walking
minutes playing fetch	**minutes walking**
f	w
20	76
25	95
40	152
50	190

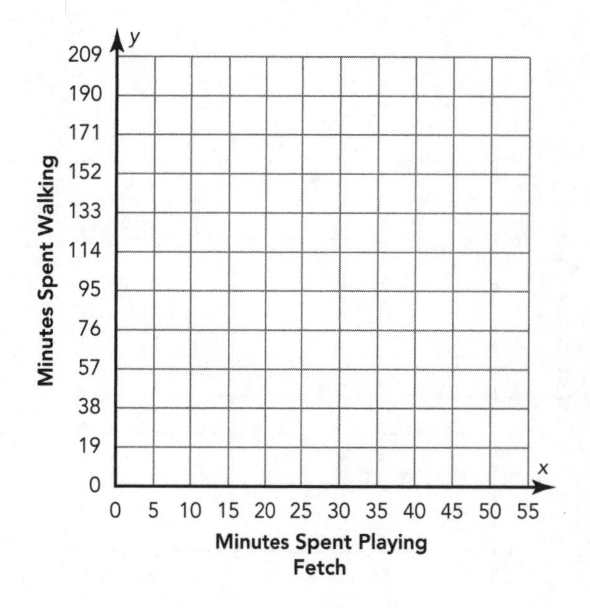

7. This year, you started working in the writing lab. You help fellow students improve the essays and reports they are writing. You charge $12 for 5 hours of tutoring. The table displays the possible number of hours spent tutoring and the number of dollars charged.

Number of Hours Spent Tutoring	Number of Dollars Charged
hours	dollars
h	d
10	24
25	60
35	84
50	120

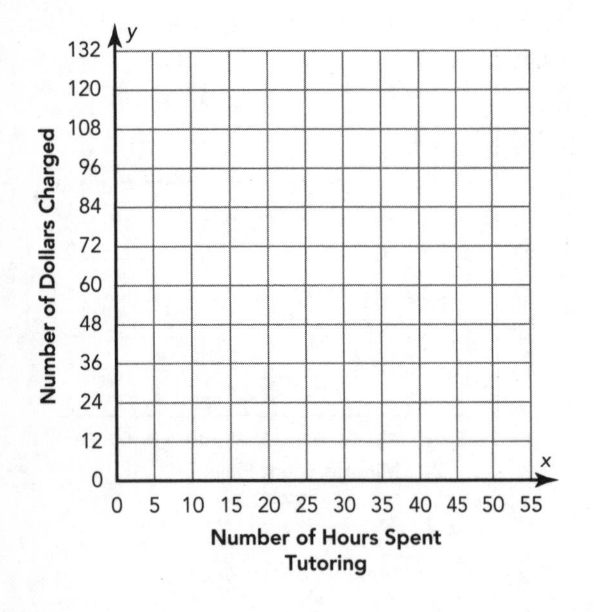

8. Rebecca is putting together packages of items for a joke shop. She has to make sure each package contains 18 fake spiders and 11 rubber snakes. The table displays the possible number of rubber snakes and the number of fake spiders in a package.

Number of Rubber Snakes	Number of Fake Spiders
snakes	spiders
r	f
44	72
77	126
88	144
110	180

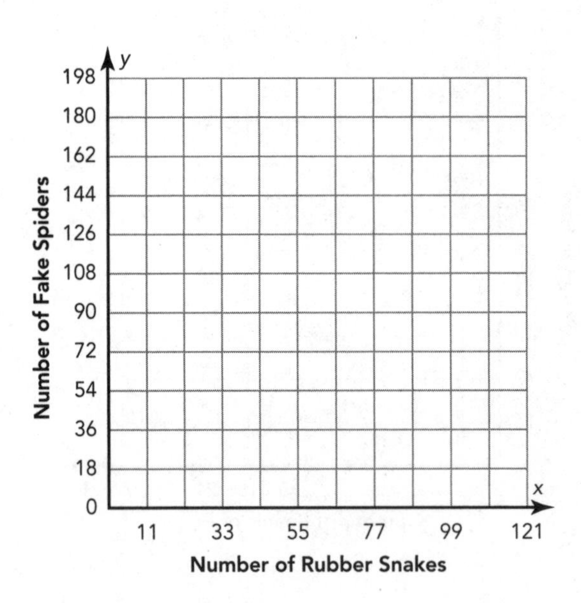

Name ______________________________ Date ______________

9. Tremaine is making bird feed. For every 6 tablespoons of corn kernels, he puts in 11 tablespoons of sunflower seeds. The table displays the possible number of tablespoons of corn kernels and the number of tablespoons of sunflower seeds in a mixture.

Number of Tablespoons of Sunflower Seeds	Number of Tablespoons of Corn Kernels
tablespoons of seeds	tablespoons of kernels
s	k
22	12
77	42
88	48
99	54

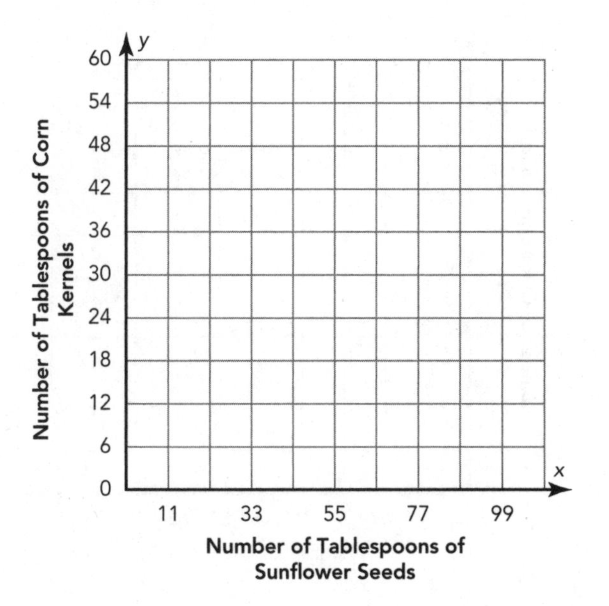

10. Your uncle works as an operations scheduler for a company that manufactures air filters. The company manufactures two metal mesh filters for every three carbon filters. The table displays the possible number of carbon filters manufactured and the number of metal mesh filters manufactured.

Number of Carbon Filters Manufactured	Number of Metal Mesh Filters Manufactured
carbon filters	metal mesh filters
c	m
6	4
15	10
24	16
27	18

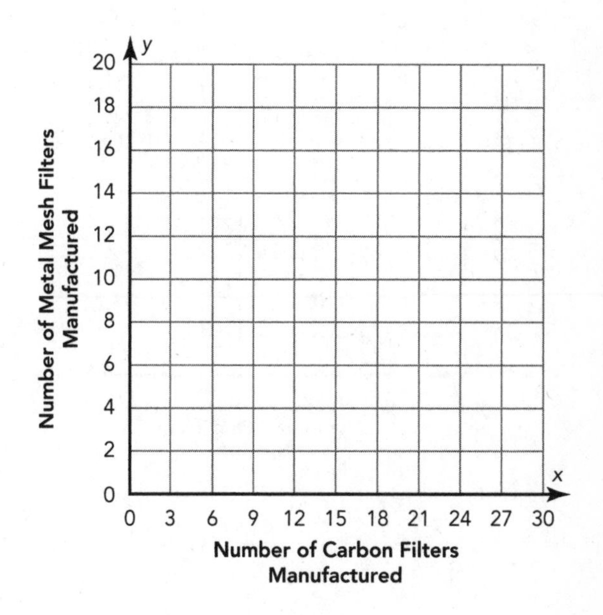

11. You are involved in a community tree-planting project. At each planting site, you plant 11 oak trees for every 3 pine trees. The table displays the possible number of pine trees planted and the number of oak trees planted.

Number of Pine Trees Planted	Number of Oak Trees Planted
pine trees	oak trees
p	k
12	44
18	66
24	88
30	110

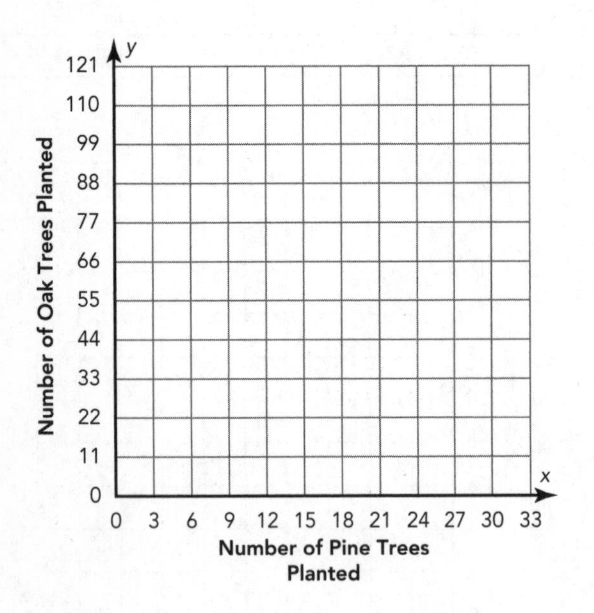

12. Crystal is studying to become a geologist. For every 4 hours of classroom instruction she receives on earth processes, she also receives 9 hours of lab instruction on earth materials. The table displays the possible number of classroom hours and the number of lab hours.

Number of Lab Hours	Number of Classroom Hours
lab hours	classroom hours
b	c
27	12
54	24
72	32
81	36

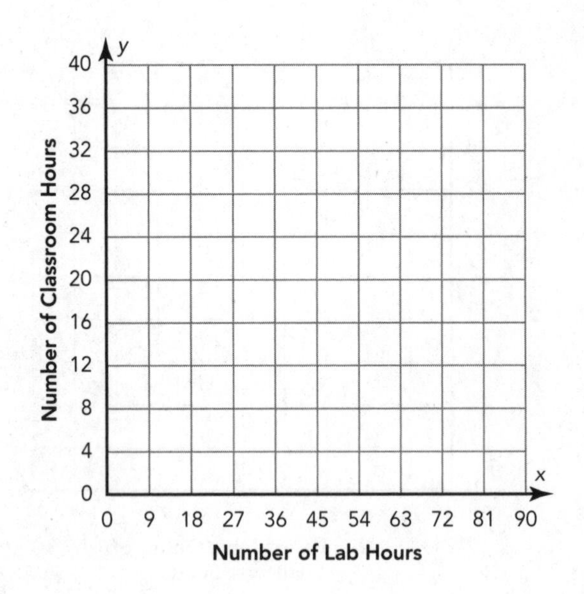

Name ______________________________ Date ______________

B. Answer each question.

1. During your morning workout, you run for 20 seconds for every 3 seconds you sprint.

a. Determine the constant of proportionality for the ratio between the number of seconds you run and the number of seconds you sprint.

b. Write a proportion that shows the relationship between the number of seconds you run, the number of seconds you sprint, and the constant of proportionality.

c. Rewrite the proportion as an equation to represent the number of seconds you run in terms of the number of seconds you sprint.

2. Lewis had pictures taken for his football team. The pictures come in different sizes. The ratio of each picture is a height of 7 inches by a width of 6 inches.

a. Determine the constant of proportionality for the ratio between the height of each picture, in inches, and the width of each picture, in inches.

b. Write a proportion that shows the relationship between the height of each picture, the width of each picture, and the constant of proportionality.

c. Rewrite the proportion as an equation to represent the height of each picture in terms of the width of each picture.

3. Francis played tennis for two hours. His activity watch showed that he burned 17 calories every 5 minutes.

a. Determine the constant of proportionality for the ratio between the number of calories burned and the time Francis played tennis, in minutes.

b. Write a proportion that shows the relationship between the number of calories burned, the time Francis played tennis, and the constant of proportionality.

c. Rewrite the proportion that shows the relationship between the number of calories burned in terms of the number of minutes Francis played tennis.

4. Your class is going on a field trip to an art museum. For every 6 students going to the museum, there is 1 adult chaperone.

a. Determine the constant of proportionality for the ratio between the number of students who visit the museum and the number of adults who visit the museum.

b. Write a proportion that shows the relationship between the number of students, the number of adults, and the constant of proportionality.

c. Rewrite the proportion as an equation to represent the number of students in terms of the number of adults.

Name ______________________________ Date ______________

5. Daniel is decorating mirrors from a craft kit he received. He can decorate 10 mirrors every 3 hours.
   a. Determine the constant of proportionality for the ratio between the number of mirrors he decorates and the time it takes, in hours.

   b. Write a proportion that shows the relationship between the number of mirrors he decorates and the time it takes, and the constant of proportionality.

   c. Rewrite the proportion as an equation to represent the number of mirrors he decorates in terms of the time, in minutes.

6. Caleb is a landscaper. He knows that for every 25 pounds of topsoil he orders he can cover an area of 13 square feet.
   a. Determine the constant of proportionality for the ratio between the number of pounds of topsoil and the area it covers, in square feet.

   b. Write a proportion that shows the relationship between the number of pounds of topsoil, the area it covers, and the constant of proportionality.

   c. Rewrite the proportion as an equation to represent the number of pounds of topsoil in terms of the area, in square feet.

7. You work at an ice cream store and you are ordering more ice cream. The ice cream comes in cases. In each case there are 3 containers of chocolate ice cream for every 2 containers of vanilla ice cream.

a. Determine the constant of proportionality for the ratio between the number of containers of chocolate ice cream and the number of containers of vanilla ice cream.

b. Write a proportion that shows the relationship between the number of chocolate ice cream containers, the number of vanilla ice cream containers, and the constant of proportionality.

c. Rewrite the proportion as an equation to represent the number of chocolate ice cream containers in terms of the number of vanilla ice cream containers.

8. Louis knows he must practice his serves to get better at tennis. For every 15 minutes he practices, 11 minutes are spent practicing serves.

a. Determine the constant of proportionality for the ratio between the total number of minutes spent practicing and the number of minutes spent practicing serves.

b. Write a proportion that shows the relationship between the total number of minutes spent practicing, the number of minutes spent practicing serves, and the constant of proportionality.

c. Rewrite the proportion as an equation to represent the total number of minutes spent practicing in terms of the number of minutes spent practicing serves.

Name ____________________ Date ____________

9. To make the perfect shade of purple paint, Shawn uses 5 parts of red paint for every 6 parts of blue paint.

   a. Determine the constant of proportionality for the ratio between the number of parts of red paint and number of parts of blue paint.

   b. Write a proportion that shows the relationship between the number of parts of red paint, the number of parts of blue paint, and the constant of proportionality.

   c. Rewrite the proportion as an equation to represent the number of parts of red paint in terms of the number of parts of blue paint.

10. Scott is trying to help the environment. He decides that for every 1 plastic bag he uses, he will recycle 17 plastic bottles.

   a. Determine the constant of proportionality for the ratio between the number of plastic bags Scott uses and the number of plastic bottles he recycles.

   b. Write a proportion that shows the relationship between the number of plastic bags Scott uses, the number of plastic bottles he recycles, and the constant of proportionality.

   c. Rewrite the proportion as an equation to represent the number of plastic bags Scott uses in terms of the number of plastic bottles he recycles.

11. Louis owns his own orchard. He plants 9 fruit trees for every 5 nut trees.

a. Determine the constant of proportionality for the ratio between the number of fruit trees planted and the number of nut trees planted.

b. Write a proportion that shows the relationship between the number of fruit trees planted, the number of nut trees planted, and the constant of proportionality.

c. Rewrite the proportion as an equation to represent the number of fruit trees planted in terms of the number of nut trees planted.

12. For every $20 you earn, you donate $3 to charity.

a. Determine the constant of proportionality for the ratio between the amount you earn, in dollars, and the amount you donate to charity, in dollars.

b. Write a proportion that shows the relationship between the amount you earn, the amount you donate, and the constant of proportionality.

c. Rewrite the proportion as an equation to represent the amount you earn in terms of the amount you donate.

Name ______________________________ Date ______________

C. Determine whether each graph represents a direct variation relationship.

1.

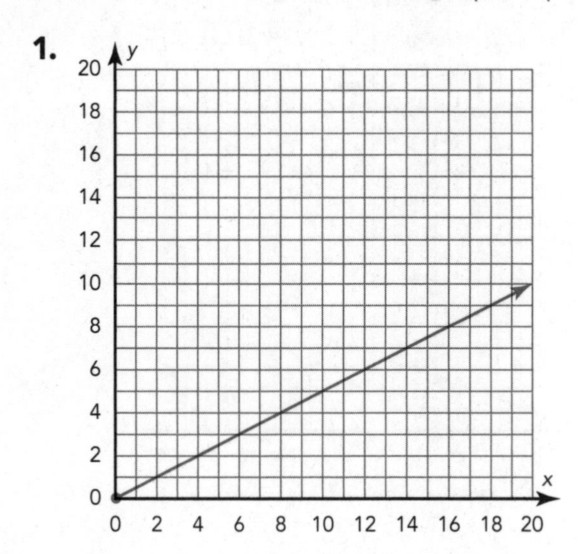

2.

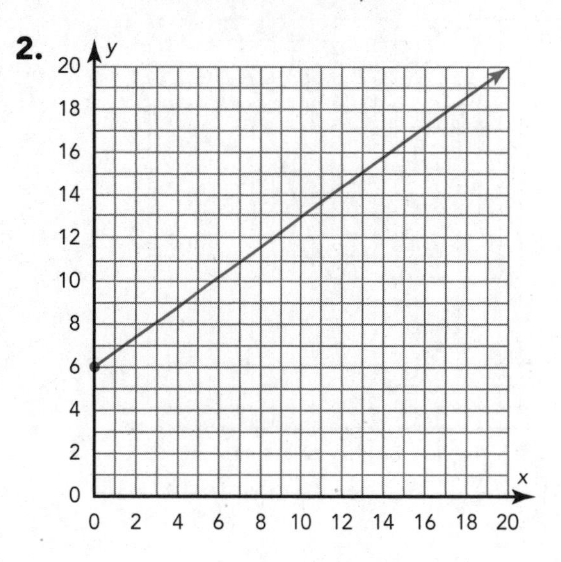

3.

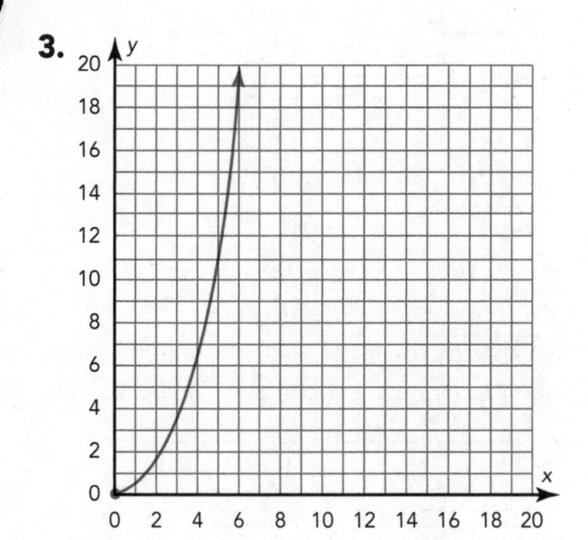

4.

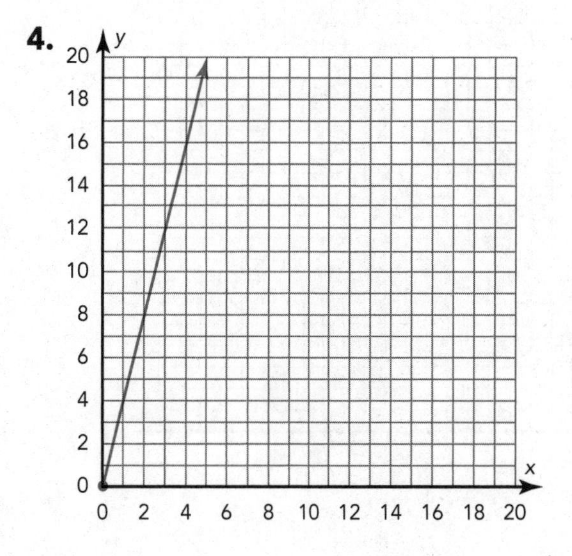

5.

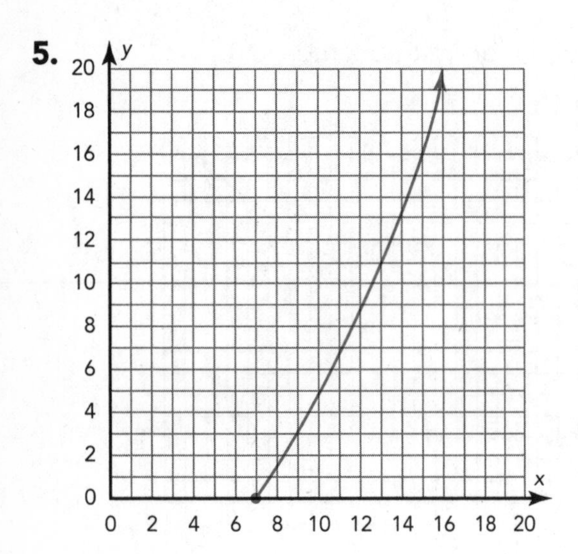
y
x
0
2
4
6
8
10
12
14
16
18
20

6.

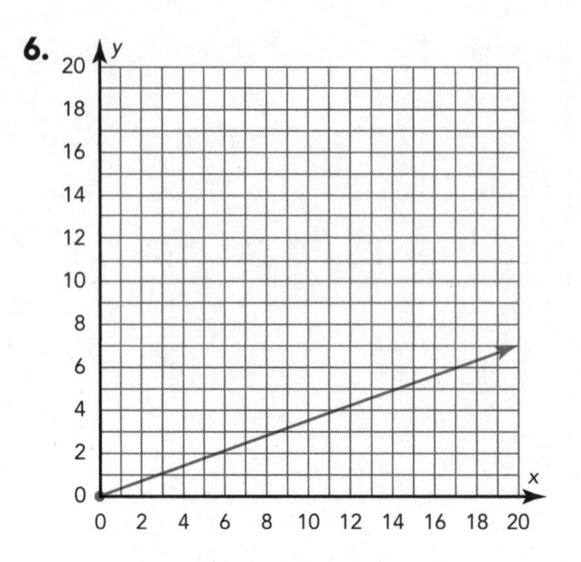
y
x
0
2
4
6
8
10
12
14
16
18
20

7.

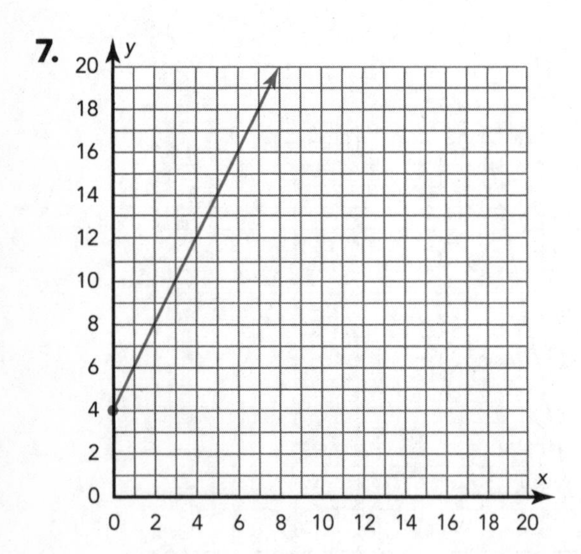
y
x
0
2
4
6
8
10
12
14
16
18
20

8.

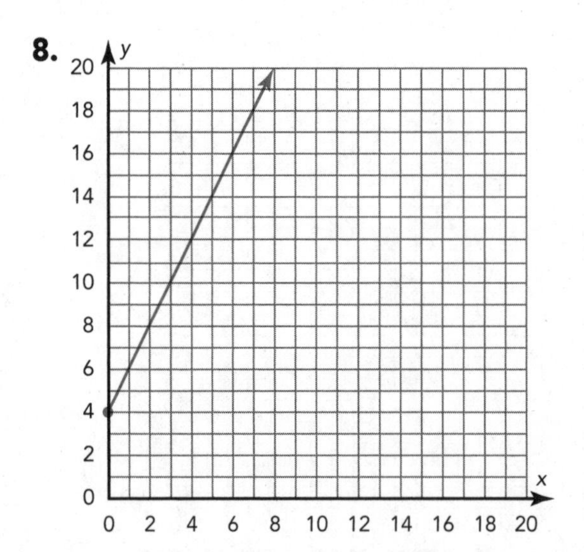
y
x
0
2
4
6
8
10
12
14
16
18
20

Name ____________________ Date ____________

9.

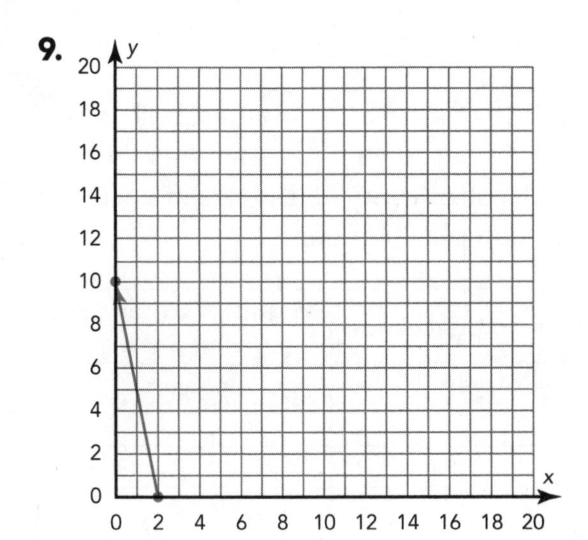

10.

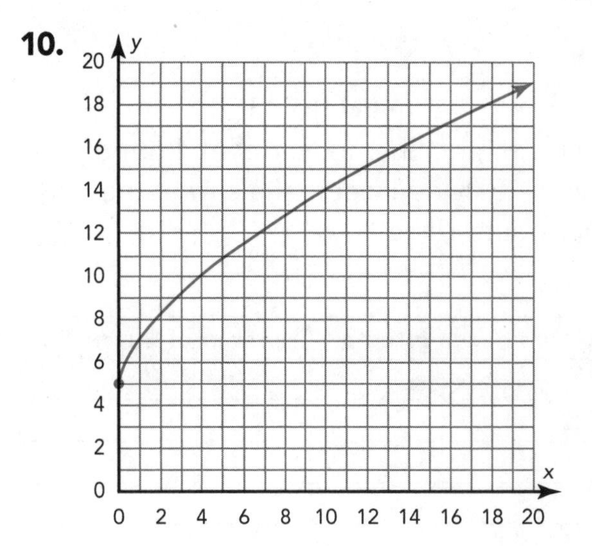

11.

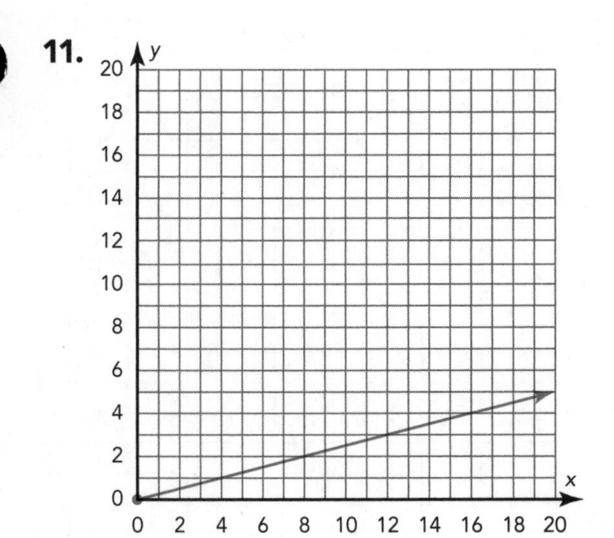

12.

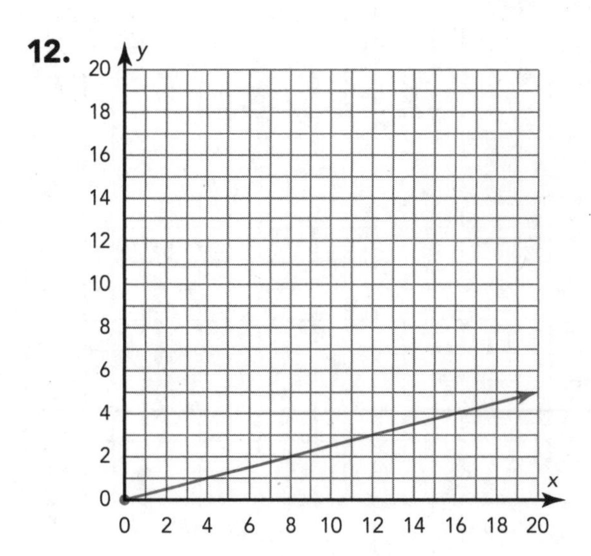

D. Complete each table. Then, use the table to draw a graph of each relationship.

1. Jessica spent many days at the city park last summer. She noticed that 4 out of every 15 flying insects she saw at the park were butterflies.

Number of Insects	Number of Butterflies
insects	butterflies

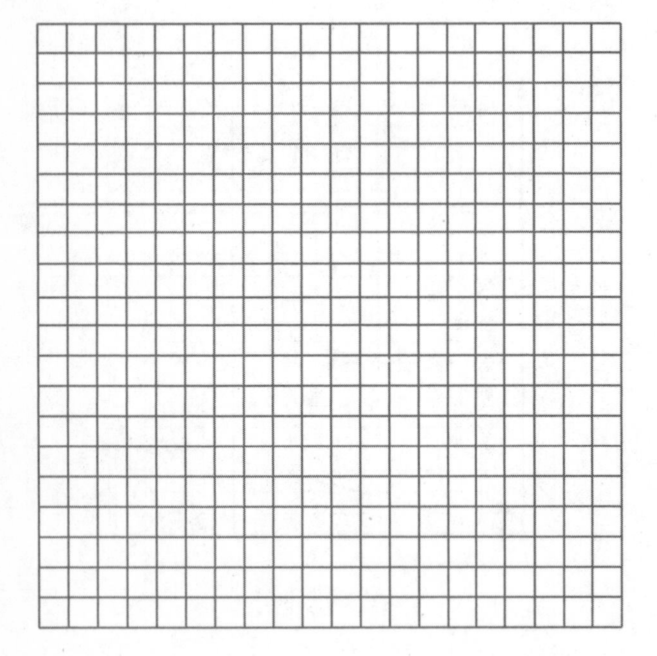

2. Sylvia is in charge of all the baseball leagues in her town. She estimates that about 1 out of every 15 players in each league can play first base.

Players in the League	Players Who can Play First Base
players	players

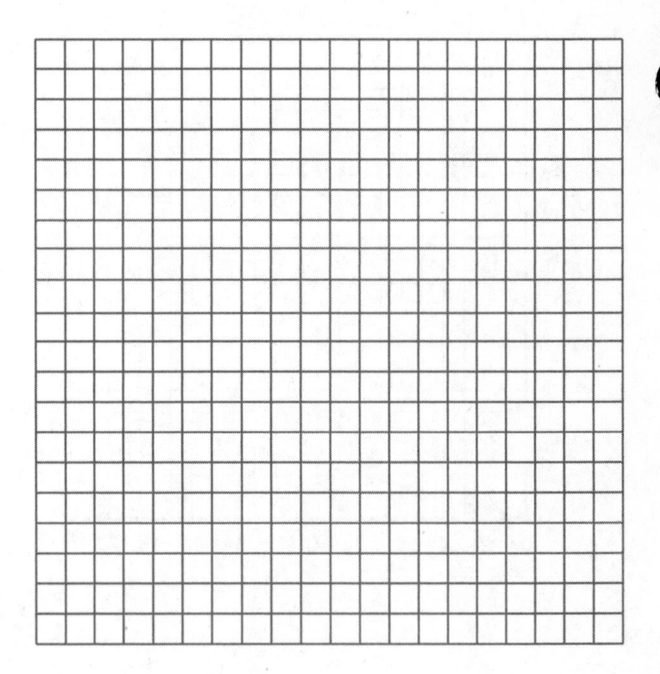

Name ______________________________ Date ______________

3. Your cousin plays shooting guard for his community basketball team. When he plays in a game, 3 out of every 5 baskets he scores for his team are jump-shots.

Total Baskets	Jump-Shots
baskets	jump-shots

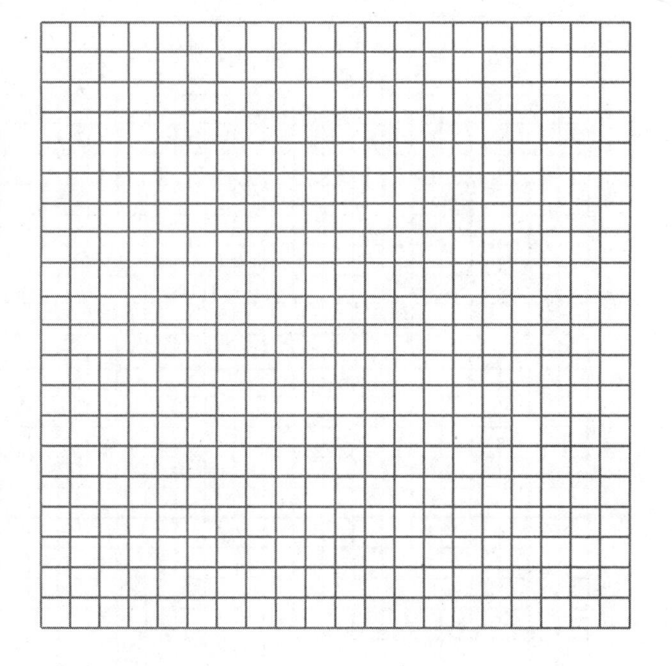

4. Ada looked at her household budget for the past several months and determined that 1 out of every 8 dollars she spent on groceries were spent on whole fruits and vegetables.

Amount Spent on Groceries	Amount Spent on Whole Fruits and Vegetables
dollars	dollars

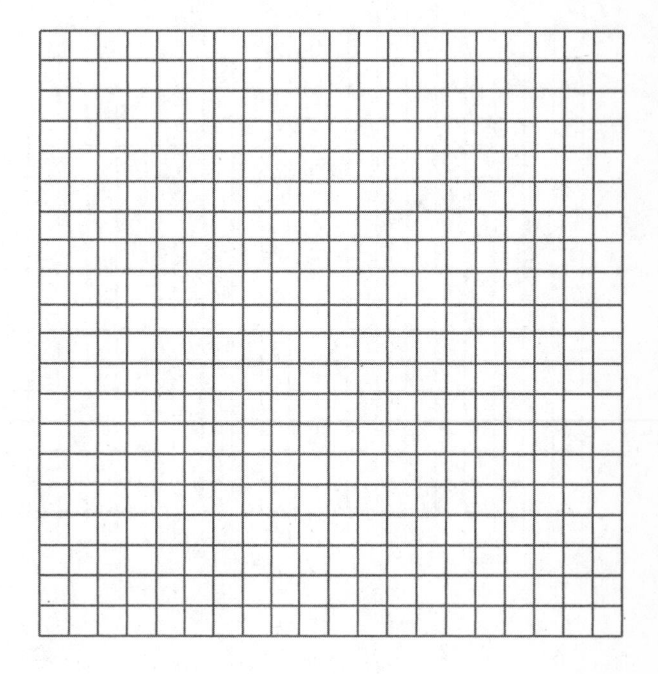

5. Latrell keeps all of his line drawings in portfolio folders. He notices as he sorts through the drawings that, in each folder, 2 out of every 5 drawings are still lifes.

Total Drawings	Still Lifes
drawings	still lifes

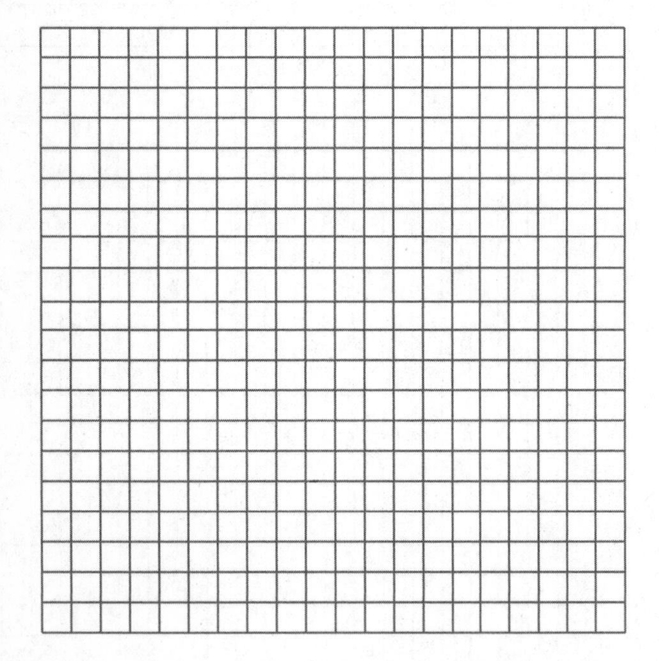

6. Russell looked at his household budget for the past several months and determined that 4 out of every 9 dollars he spent on groceries were spent on high protein foods.

Amount Spent on Groceries	Amount Spent on High Protein Foods
dollars	dollars

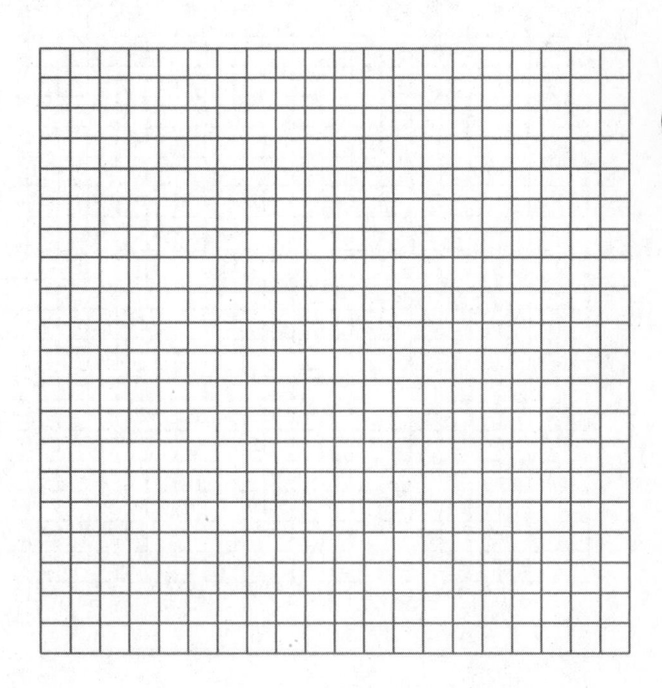

Name ______________________________ Date ______________

7. Lois keeps track of the yards gained or lost each quarter for the Silver Stripes football team. She noticed that 1 out of every 3 yards lost by the Stripes were due to the slippery conditions of the rainy game.

Total Yards Lost	Yards Lost Due to Slippery Conditions
yards	yards

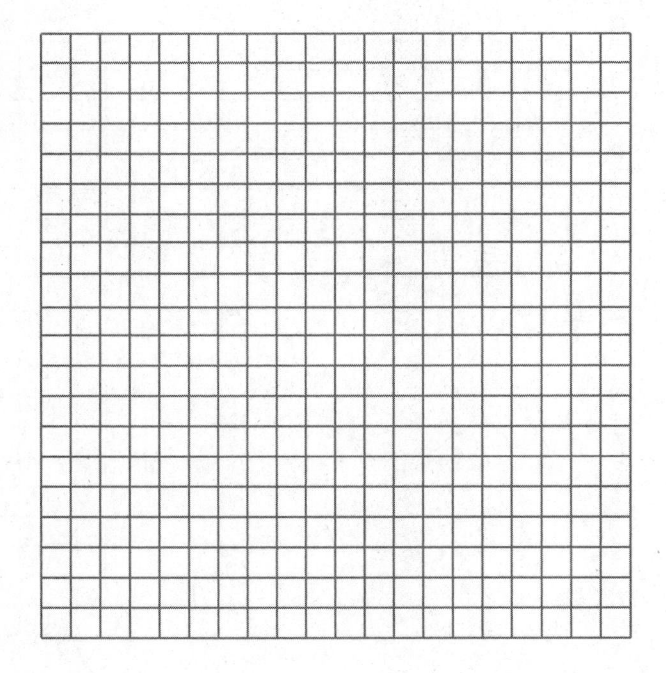

8. You maintain inventory for a local craft store. You notice that typically 5 out of 9 items on backorder are for one of the store's customers, Ms. Bestwick.

Items on Backorder	Ms. Bestwick's Items
items	items

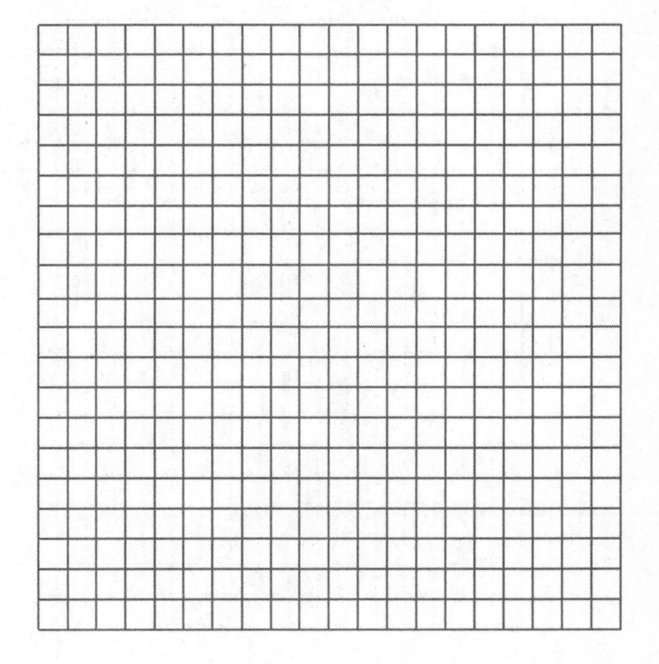

9. At the last Ferndale Middle School dance, only 2 out of 7 students actually danced, while the rest stood around.

Total Students	Students Who Danced
students	students

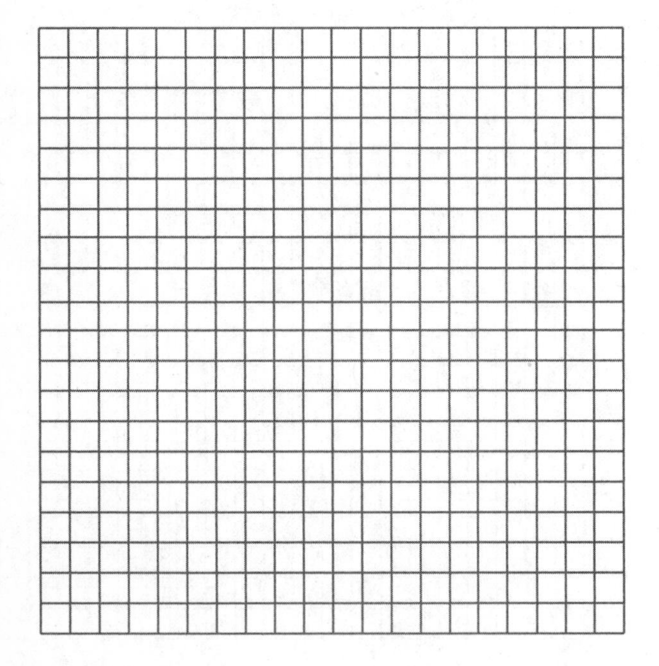

10. You are an environmentalist that is recording the number of abandoned nesting sites for herons in areas of wetlands. You find that, on average, 1 out of every 4 nesting sites have been abandoned.

Total Sites	Abandoned Sites
sites	sites

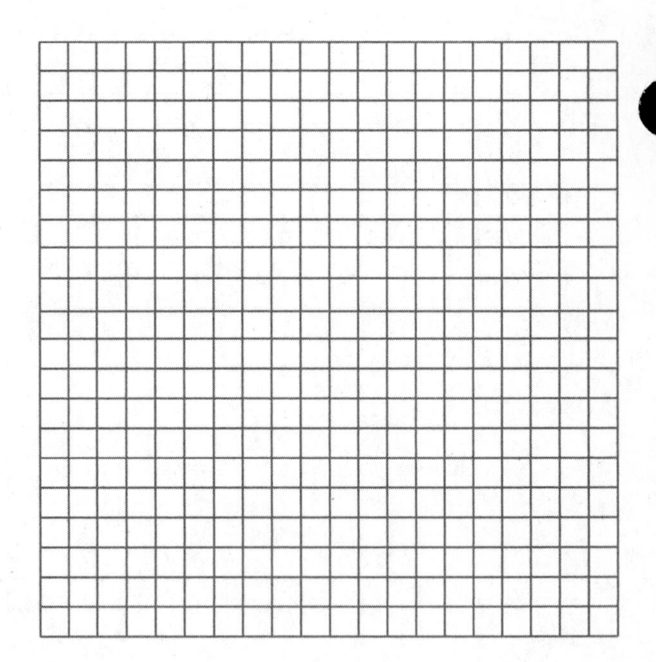

Name ______________________________ Date ______________

11. Marian's printer mangles 1 out of 5 pages while doing a printing job.

Number of Pages in Report	Number of Pages Mangled
pages	pages

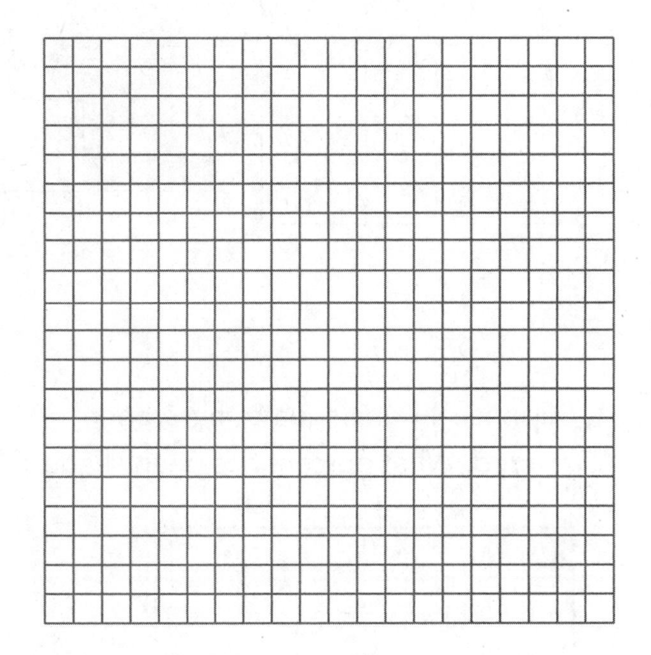

12. Norman owes his parents money, and 6 out of every 7 dollars of his total debt came about because of the time he wrecked their snowmobile.

Total Debt	Debt From Snowmobile
dollars	dollars

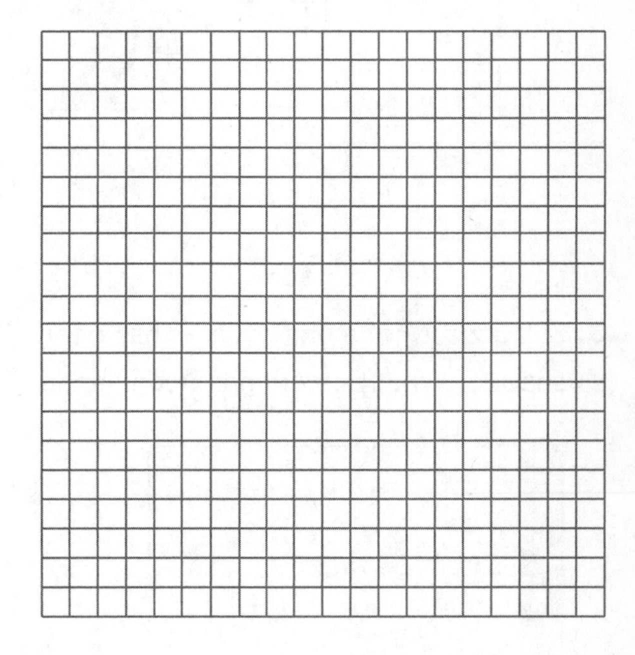

Topic 4

Proportional Relationships

Name ______________________________ Date ________________

I. Fractional Percent Models

A. The grid in each model represents 1 whole. Determine each percent.

1. Suppose $\frac{3}{5}$ of a unit square has been shaded. What percent has been shaded?

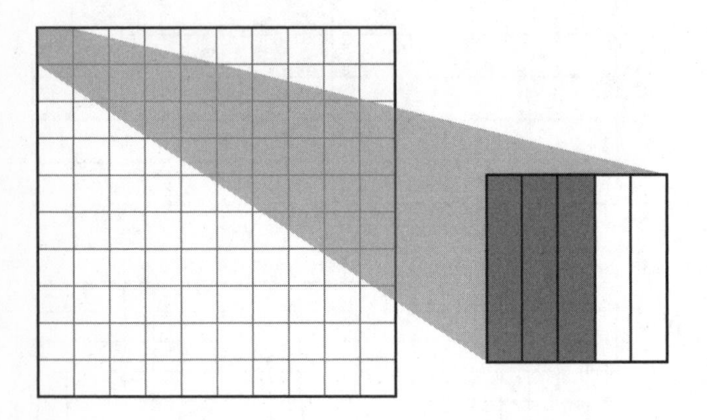

2. Suppose $\frac{3}{4}$ of a unit square has been shaded. What percent has been shaded?

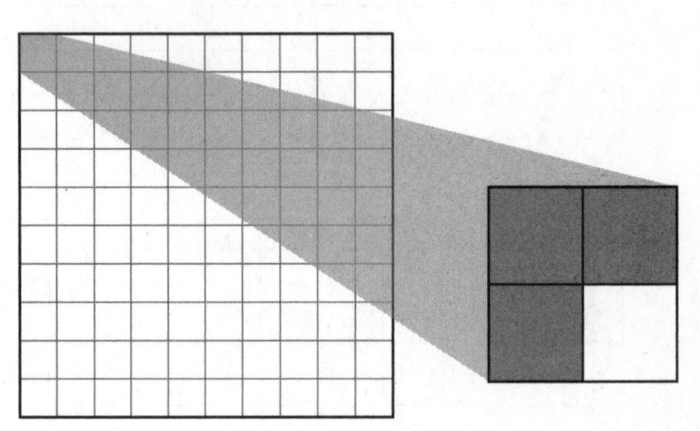

3. Suppose $7\frac{1}{2}$ of a unit squares has been shaded. What percent has been shaded?

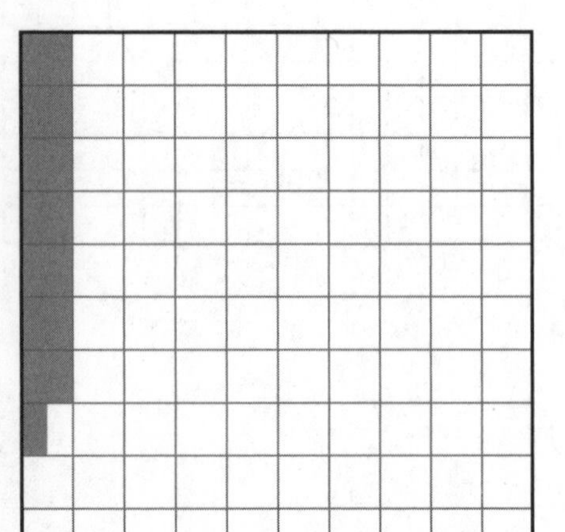

4. Suppose $1\frac{1}{5}$ unit squares have been shaded. What percent has been shaded?

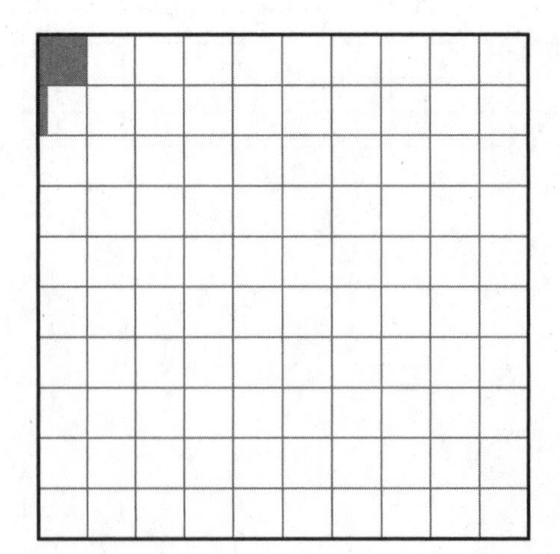

Name ______________________________ Date ______________

5. Suppose $\frac{3}{10}$ of a unit square has been shaded. What percent has been shaded?

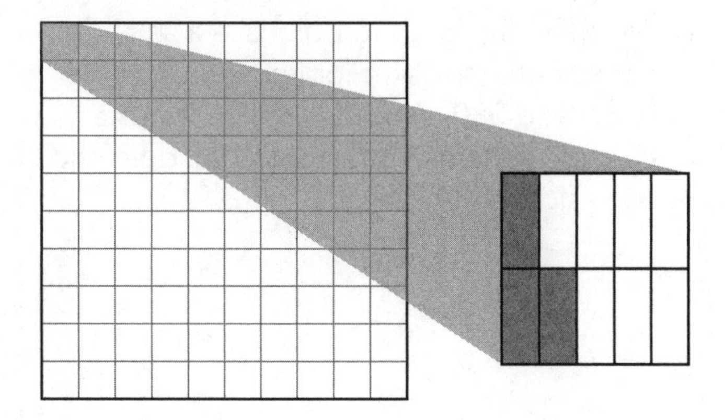

6. Suppose $8\frac{1}{4}$ unit squares have been shaded. What percent has been shaded?

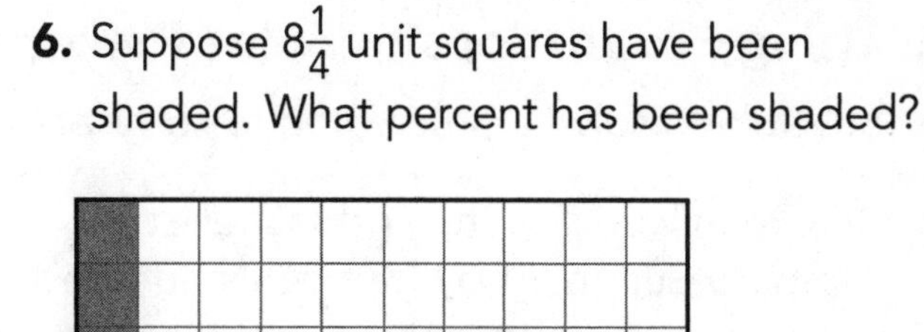

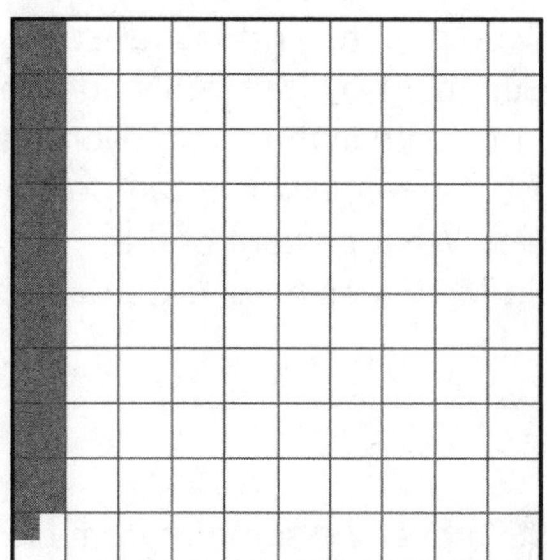

B. Rewrite each number as a fraction, a decimal, and a percent. If the number is a fractional percent, rewrite it as a percent with a decimal. If the number is a decimal percent, rewrite it as a percent with a fraction.

1. $\frac{2}{100}$

2. 1.06

3. $\frac{4}{5}\%$

4. 0.2%

5. 6.7%

6. $90\frac{3}{10}\%$

7. $\frac{6}{500}$

8. 0.055

9. $\frac{1}{2}\%$

10. 0.75%

11. 0.006

11. $1\frac{7}{1000}$

II. Using Proportions to Solve Percent Problems

A. Set up and solve a proportion to solve each problem.

1. Mr. Green works as the art teacher at Hamburg Summer Day Camp. Six hundred campers participate in the camp every day. Yesterday Mr. Green helped 6 campers on an art project. What percent of the campers did Mr. Green help yesterday?

2. Jonah is saving up to purchase a small flat screen television for his bedroom. He has saved $80, which is 64% of the total cost of the television. How much does the television cost?

3. Ben saved $75 over the summer from his part-time job. He withdrew 40% of the money to buy new clothes. The rest of the money he kept in his bank account. How much money did Ben spend on new clothes?

4. Samantha raises animals and trains them to appear in Hollywood movies. Currently, 23 of her penguins are appearing in a film about global freezing. That is 92% of the penguins Samantha has raised. How many penguins has she raised?

5. Mr. Ivey teaches dance at the middle school. His classes are 90 minutes long, and he spends 94% of class time teaching strength and conditioning. How many minutes do Mr. Ivey's students spend on strength and conditioning in each class?

6. Christopher plays quarterback for a neighborhood football team. During his team's first game, he executed 60 plays, 42 of which were successful. What percent of Christopher's plays were successful?

Name ______________________________ Date ______________

B. Set up and solve a proportion to solve each problem.

1. What is 78% of 50?

2. What is 54% of 450?

3. The number 110 is what percent of 500?

4. The number 21 is what percent of 75?

5. The number 88 is 44% of what number?

6. The number 57 is 76% of what number?

C. Solve each problem.

1. Carlos purchased an antique chair for $15. He later sold the chair for $27 to an antique dealer. What was the percent markup of the chair?

2. Lamar purchases comic books at garage sales and marks them up 75% before reselling them to comic book dealers. If Lamar purchases a comic book at a garage sale for $4, how much will he charge the comic book dealer for it?

3. You want to leave a tip for a meal that costs $17.95. If all you have is $3.00, what percentage tip will you be able to leave?

4. Jeremy bought a souvenir while on vacation. The item cost $22, but the total bill was $23.43. What percent was the sales tax?

5. Shalinda wants to leave an 18% tip for her meal. If her meal cost $25.10, what should be the total she pays, including the tip?

6. Karen buys a sweatshirt for $30. The sales tax in her state is 7%. What is the total amount Karen will pay for the sweatshirt, including sales tax?

7. If a store marks up the price of an item by 45% and sells it to customers for $58, what was the original price the store paid for the item?

8. Lin paid $3.30 in sales tax on an item that cost $60. What percent sales tax did he pay?

9. Yolanda always tips her hair stylist 22% of whatever her services cost. On her most recent trip to her hair stylist, the services Yolanda received cost $150. What amount should Yolanda tip her hair stylist?

10. The Fishers ate out at a restaurant and paid a total of $68.22, including the tip. If the Fishers tipped 20%, what was the cost of the meal?

III. Percent Increase and Percent Decrease

A. Determine each percent increase or percent decrease.

1. The local animal shelter had 12 dogs at the beginning of the week. Since then, the number of dogs at the shelter has decreased by 9. What is the percent change in the number of dogs at the animal shelter this week?

2. Haley has a collection of necklaces. Last month, she had 40 necklaces. She now has 76 necklaces. What is the percent change in the number of necklaces in Haley's collection from last month to now?

3. Last month, Ebony had 72 dollars in a checking account. The current balance is 126 dollars. What is the percent change in the account balance from last month to this month?

4. Last month, you conducted a survey for the student newspaper. Of the students that you surveyed, 20 thought that the student council president was doing a good job. You conduct the same survey this month. After surveying the same students, you find that 11 think that the student council president is doing a good job. What is the percent change in the number of students who think that the student council president is doing a good job from last month to this month?

Name ______________________________ Date ______________

5. Last season, your favorite basketball team won 20 games. So far this season, your favorite basketball team has won 31 games. What is the percent change in the number of games that your favorite team won from last season to this season?

6. Evita collects baseball cards and is trying to complete a special edition set of cards. Last month, she collected 25 cards. This month, she collected 19 cards. What is the percent change in the number of cards collected from last month to this month?

7. The Italian restaurant near your house sold 60 plain pizzas last week. They sold 39 fewer plain pizzas this week than last week. What is the percent change in the number of plain pizzas sold from last week to this week?

8. At the beginning of the month, Rachel's Used Car Dealership had 80 cars on the lot. Today, there are 100 cars on the lot. What is the percent change in the number of cars on the lot this month?

9. Last month, you joined an online strategy game. When you joined, there were 25 members. This month, there are 47 members. What is the percent change in the number of members from last month to this month?

10. At Joy's Toy Store, their most popular toy sold is a scooter. Last summer, the toy store sold 20 scooters. This summer, the store sold 27 scooters. What is the percent change in the number of scooters sold from last summer to this summer?

11. The peach tree in Anthony's back yard produced 56 pounds of peaches in one summer. The next summer, it produced 14 pounds less than the previous year. What is the percent change in the number of pounds of peaches produced from one summer to the next?

12. In summer, you want to put the wind chill factor to work for you. You know that using ceiling fans can make you feel 23 degrees cooler in a house that is 92 degrees, so you turn on your ceiling fans. What is the percent change in the temperature after the ceiling fans are turned on?

B. Answer each question.

1. Mr. Tate opened a new general store in the downtown area. On the day of the grand opening, he had 10 customers. The next day, he had 80% more customers than on the grand opening day. How many customers did Mr. Tate have on the second day?

2. Dante creates pottery. He brought 40 pieces to a show at the fall festival. When he went to the spring carnival, he brought 15% more pieces than he brought to the fall festival. How many pieces of pottery did Dante bring to the spring carnival?

3. Kulas Recital Hall is located on the campus of Oberlin Conservatory of Music in Oberlin, Ohio. One day before a piano recital was to take place, 30 tickets had been sold. Happily for the concert organizers an additional 80% of the 30 seats that were previously sold were sold on the actual day of the concert. The result was a sell-out. How many seats does Kulas Recital Hall have?

4. Matthew is scaling down a photograph that has an area of 8 square inches. He plans to reduce its area by 25%. What will be the area in square inches of the reduced photograph?

5. The heart of a black bear beats about 50 times per minute during normal sleep in the fall. When the animal hibernates in winter, its heart rate decrease by 84%. How many times per minute does a black bear's heart beat during hibernation?

6. Your aunt is a web designer. When she tones a photo for a website, she works with it in an image quality of 25 dots per inch (dpi). When she uploads it to the website, she reduces the quality by 60%. What is the dpi your aunt uses for a photo that she uploads to a website?

Name ______________________________ Date ______________

7. Your sister works as a tutor in the evenings. Last school year she charged $25 per hour for her services. After taking some certification classes over the summer, she increased her hourly charge by 40%. How much does your sister now charge per hour for her tutoring services?

8. Your MP3 player has 40 gigabytes of music on it. During the next sync, you add 10% more music to it, and it is full. How many gigabytes does the MP3 player hold now?

9. The local take-out pizza place sold 50 pepperoni pizzas last month. They sold 6% more pepperoni pizzas this month than last month. How many pepperoni pizzas did they sell this month?

10. Last season, your favorite hockey team won 20 games. So far this season, the team has won 90% more games than last season. How many games has your favorite team won so far this season?

11. Shannon has a collection of sports cards. Last month, she had 50 sports cards. Since last month, her collection has decreased by 46%. How many sports cards does Shannon have now?

12. Each morning, Stacey makes 20 cinnamon bagels for his customers at Barney's Bagels. Because of a recent increase in the popularity of cinnamon bagels, she has increased the number she bakes each morning by 80%. How many cinnamon bagels does Stacey now bake each day?

IV. Scale Drawings

A. Solve each problem.

1. Marion is helping to organize Family Fun Day at the local park. Marion is responsible for organizing the relay race. On a map of the park, she plans the first leg of the relay race to start at Sunny Grove and end at the swimming pool. The second leg of the relay race will run from the swimming pool to the skating rink.

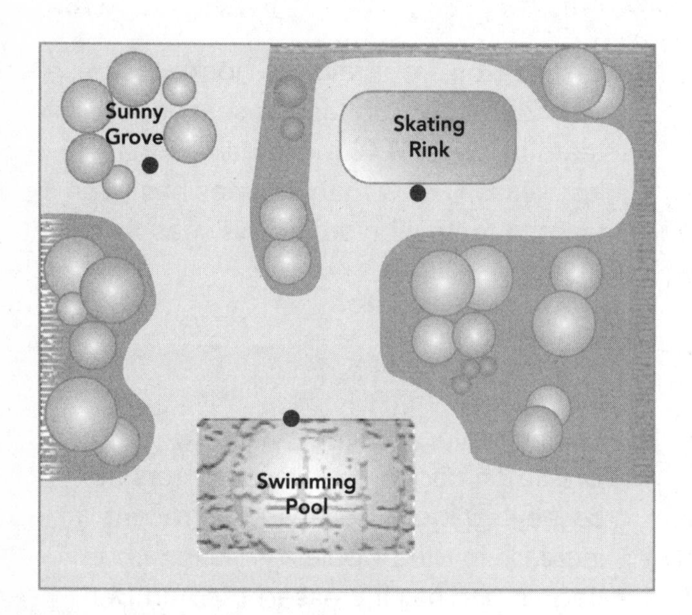

On the map:

- The distance between Sunny Grove and the swimming pool is 3.5 inches.
- The distance between the swimming pool and the skating rink is 3.2 feet.
- On the map scale, 1 in. represents 400 ft.

What is the length of the actual race?

2. Shakia enjoys planning vacations almost as much as going on them. This year, she is spending her vacation in the city. Looking at a map, she plans to start at her hotel. From there, she will go to the fine arts museum, and then to the sculpture garden. She will walk between each location.

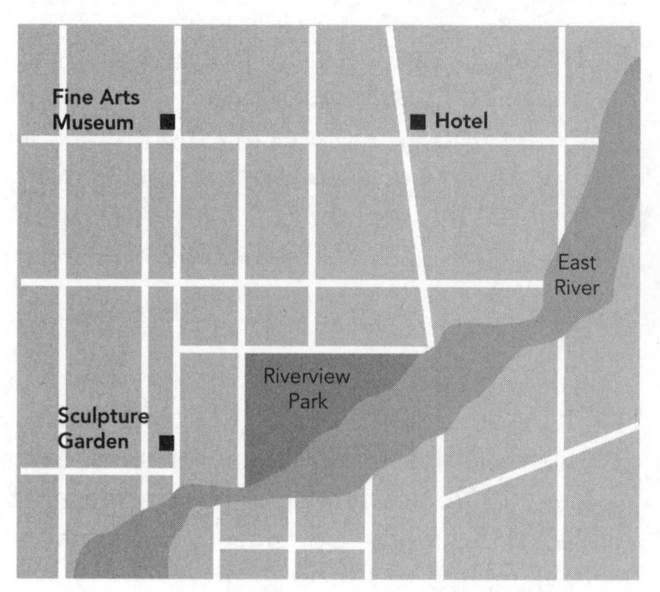

On the map:

- The distance between the hotel and the fine arts museum is 1.1 inches.
- The distance between the fine arts museum and the sculpture garden is 1.3 inches.
- On the map scale, 1 in. represents 3 km.

What is the distance that Shakia walked from the hotel to the sculpture garden?

Name ______________________________________ Date ________________

3. You have been looking forward to the music festival all year. The festival is held at the local park. Using a map of the music festival, you plan to start at the pond, where Mozart is being played. Then, you will walk to a spot in the woods, where Beethoven is being played. Finally, you'll continue to the playscape, where Bach is being played.

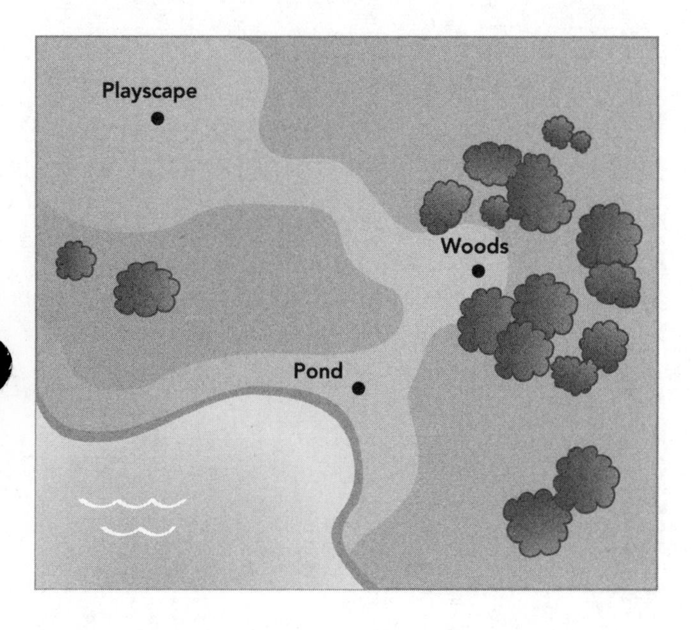

On the map:

- The distance between the pond and the woods is 1.4 inches.
- The distance between the woods and the playscape is 3.1 inches.
- On the map scale, 1 in. represents 40 yd.

What is the distance you walk from the pond to the playscape?

4. Manuel is looking at a map of his warehouse to track down shipment #452A7. He begins in the crate section. When he does not find it there, he looks among the boxes. Finally, he searches in the filing cabinets.

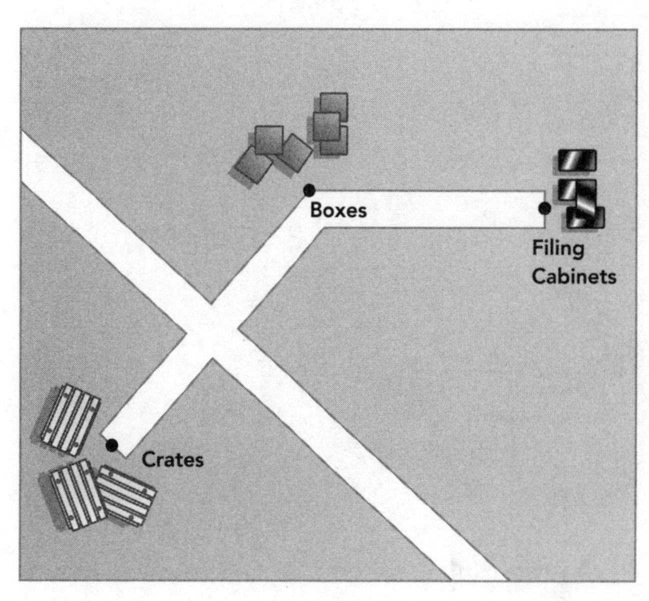

On the map:

- The distance between the crates and the boxes is 2 centimeters.
- The distance between the boxes and the filing cabinets is 1.6 centimeters.
- On the map scale, 1 cm represents 80 m.

What is the distance Manuel walks from the crates to the filing cabinets?

5. You look at a map of a department store to see how far the following three departments are from the other: Accessories, Shoes, and Clothing.

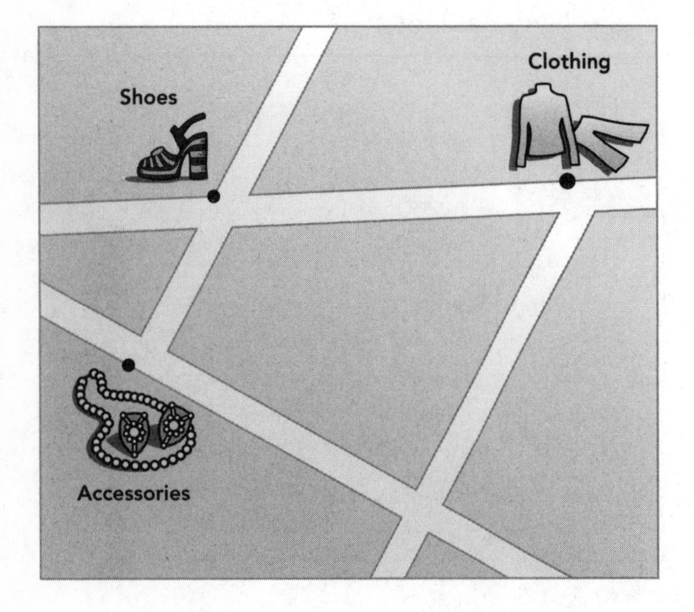

On the map:

- The distance between Accessories and Shoes is 0.5 inches.
- The distance between Shoes and Clothing is 1.2 inches.
- On the map scale, 1 in. represents 50 ft.

What is the actual distance between the shoes and the clothing departments?

6. You and your friends are at the high school football stadium watching the game. You volunteer to get snacks for yourself and your friends. You check out the map for concession stands. There are three different concessions stands. One is for drinks, one is for popcorn, and one is for the grill.

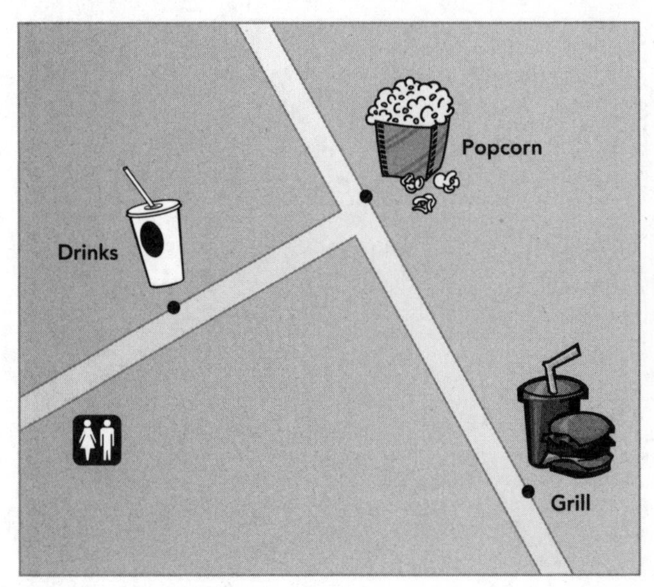

On the map:

- The distance between the drinks and the popcorn is 2 inches.
- The distance between the popcorn and the grill is 3 inches.
- On the map scale, 1 in. represents 60 ft.

What is the actual distance between the drinks and the popcorn concession stands?

Topic 1

Adding and Subtracting Rational Numbers

Name ______________________________ Date ______________

I. Using Number Lines to Add and Subtract Integers

A. Represent each sum or difference on the number line. Then, write the sum or difference.

1. $-13 + 1$

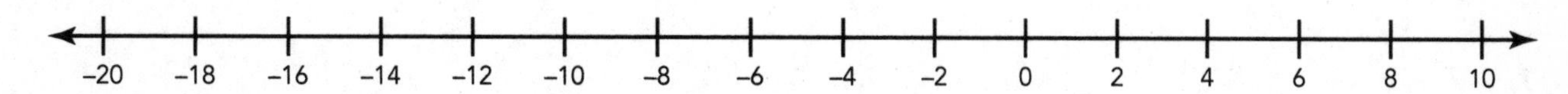

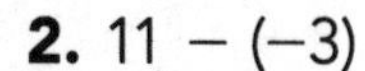

2. $11 - (-3)$

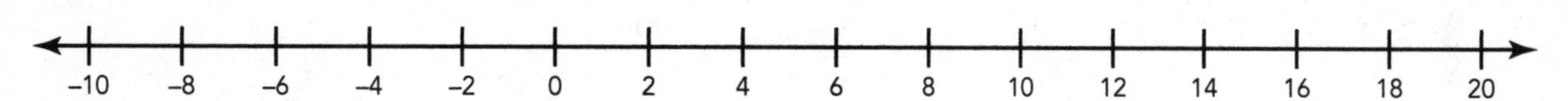

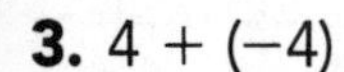

3. $4 + (-4)$

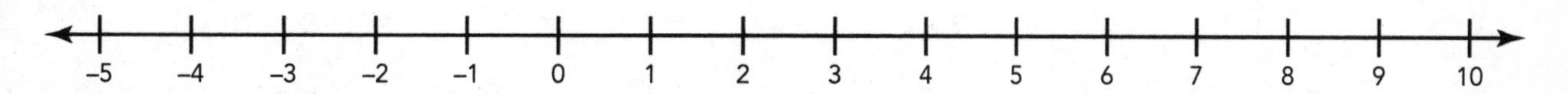

4. $-6 + 3$

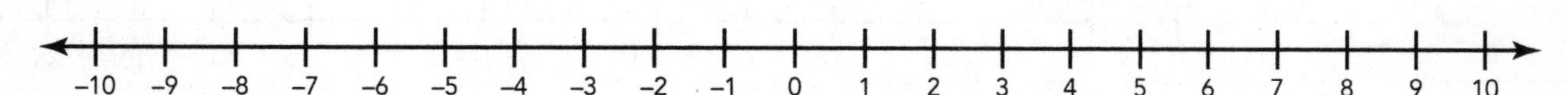

5. $11 + (-5)$

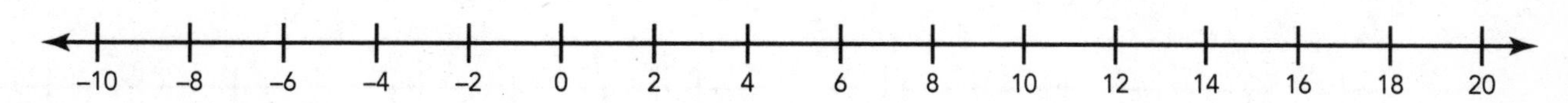

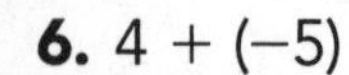

6. $4 + (-5)$

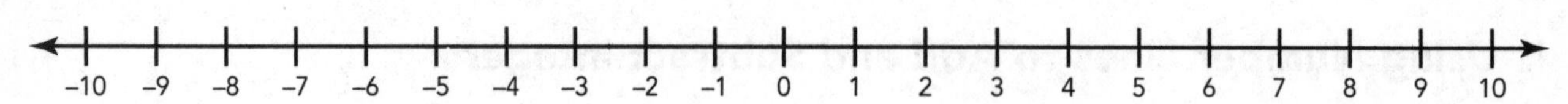

7. $-7 - 4$

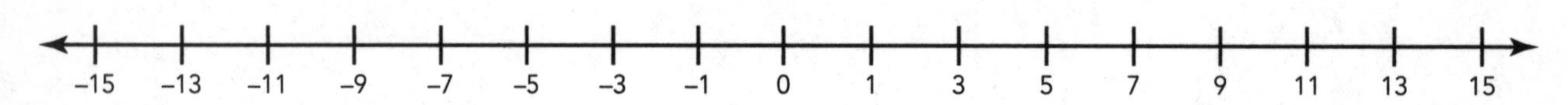

8. $2 - (-10)$

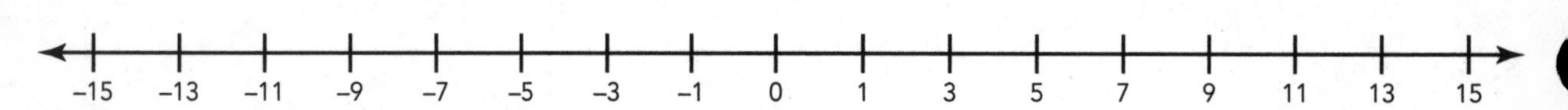

9. $-9 - (-2)$

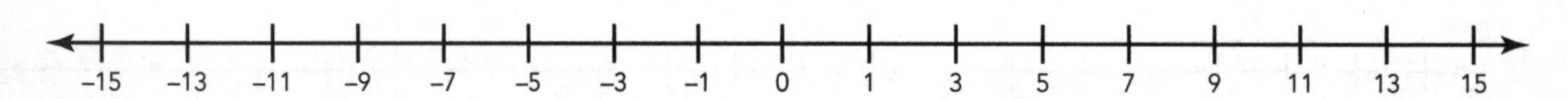

10. $8 - 12$

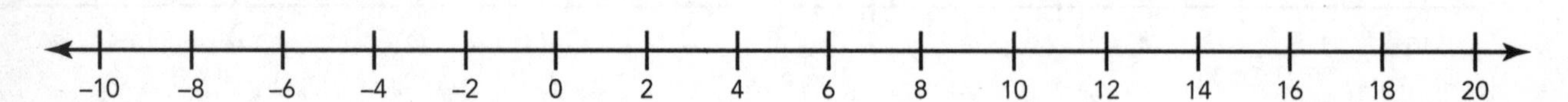

Name ______________________________ Date ______________

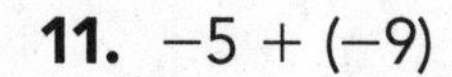

11. $-5 + (-9)$

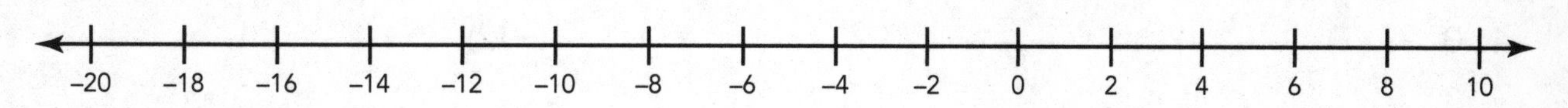

12. $-5 - 7$

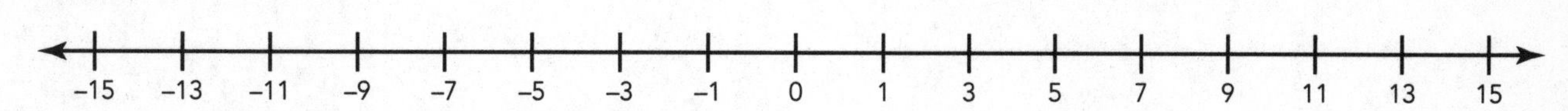

II. Adding and Subtracting Negative Integers

A. Determine each sum.

1. $0 + (-5)$

2. $-5 + (-4)$

3. $-1 + (-10)$

4. $7 + (-2)$

5. $18 + (-20)$

6. $6 + (-6)$

7. $-10 + 4$

8. $-2 + 16$

9. $-11 + (-6)$

10. $4 + (-6)$

11. $20 + (-10)$

12. $-5 + (-3)$

B. Determine each difference.

1. $0 - (-7)$

2. $-2 - (-12)$

3. $7 - (-2)$

4. $-3 - (-3)$

5. $-10 - (-5)$

6. $10 - (-6)$

7. $12 - (-8)$

8. $-8 - 14$

9. $-10 - 4$

10. $6 - (-9)$

11. $-1 - (-8)$

12. $3 - 15$

C. Complete each number sentence with + or −.

1. 7 _____ (−7) = 0

2. −4 _____ (−4) = 0

3. 2 _____ (−2) = 0

4. 13 _____ (−13) = 0

5. −9 _____ (−9) = 0

6. −1 _____ (−1) = 0

D. Determine each sum or difference.

1. $1 + (-4)$

2. $-4 + (-1)$

3. $-3 - (-11)$

4. $11 + (-1)$

Name ____________________ Date ____________

5. $6 + (-10)$

6. $5 + (-12)$

7. $8 - (-14)$

8. $-8 - (-5)$

9. $-8 + (-5)$

10. $-19 - 3$

11. $-4 + (-3)$

12. $17 - (-1)$

III. Adding and Subtracting Rational Numbers to Solve Problems

A. Sketch a model to estimate. Then, determine each solution and write an equation.

1. The temperature in Chattanooga, Tennessee, is −3°C. The temperature in Sam's hometown is 18 degrees colder than that. What is the temperature in Sam's hometown?

2. Catherine owes $22.50 on her lunch account balance. She pays $15 toward her balance. What is the status of her lunch account balance now?

3. The Subterranean roller coaster rises up to 50.6 feet above the ground before dropping 100.7 feet into an underground cavern. Describe the height of the roller coaster at the bottom of the cavern.

4. To qualify to compete in the high jump finals, athletes must jump a certain height in the semi-finals. Jon jumped $1\frac{5}{8}$ inches below the qualifying height, but his friend Anthony made it to $2\frac{1}{4}$ inches over the qualifying height. How much lower was Jon's semi-final jump compared with Anthony's?

5. A drilling crew dug to a height of $-32\frac{3}{4}$ feet during their first day of drilling. On the second day, the crew dug down $19\frac{2}{3}$ feet more than on the first day. Describe the height of the bottom of the hole after the second day.

6. The freezing point of helium is −458 degrees Fahrenheit. If you increase that temperature by 569.7 degrees Fahrenheit, you reach the freezing point of phosphorus. What is the freezing point of phosphorus?

Topic 2

Multiplying and Dividing Rational Numbers

Name ________________________________ Date ________________

I. Multiplication and Division Fact Families

A. Complete each fact family.

1. $-8 \times (-7) =$ _____

$-7 \times (-8) =$ _____

_____ $\div (-8) = -7$

$56 \div ($_____$) = -8$

2. $4 \times ($_____$) = -4$

_____ $\times 4 = -4$

$-4 \div ($_____$) = 4$

$-4 \div 4 =$ _____

3. _____ $\times 5 = -35$

_____ $\times (-7) = -35$

_____ $\div 5 = -7$

$-35 \div ($_____$) = 5$

4. $-8 \times ($_____$) = 32$

$-4 \times ($_____$) = 32$

$32 \div -8 =$ _____

$32 \div -4 =$ _____

5. $-7 \times 3 =$ _____

$3 \times (-7) =$ _____

_____ $\div (-7) = 3$

$-21 \div 3 =$ _____

6. _____ $\times (-5) = -50$

$-5 \times 10 =$ _____

$-50 \div ($_____$) = 10$

$-50 \div 10 =$ _____

7. $-12 \times (-4) =$ _____

$-4 \times (-12) =$ _____

$48 \div (-12) =$ _____

_____ $\div (-4) = -12$

8. _____ $\times (-2) = -12$

_____ $\times 6 = -12$

$-12 \div 6 =$ _____

$-12 \div$ _____ $= 6$

Name ______________________________ Date ______________

9. $-3 \times$ _____ $= -9$

$3 \times ($_____$) = -9$

_____ $\div (-3) = 3$

_____ $\div 3 = -3$

10. _____ $\times (-9) = 54$

$-9 \times$ _____ $= 54$

$54 \div ($_____$) = -6$

_____ $\div -6 = -9$

11. $10 \times ($_____$) = -20$

_____ $\times 10 = -20$

$-20 \div$ _____ $= -2$

_____ $\div -2 = 10$

12. $-11 \times 4 =$ _____

$4 \times ($_____$) = -44$

$-44 \div -11 =$ _____

$-44 \div$ _____ $= -11$

II. Multiplying and Dividing Negative Integers

A. Determine each product.

1. $2 \times (-9)$

2. $-1 \times (-6)$

3. -12×11

4. $7 \times (-6)$

5. $-3 \times (-10)$

6. -4×3

7. $11 \times (-5)$

8. $-4 \times (-9)$

9. $8 \times (-8)$

10. -25×4

11. -2×30

12. $-5 \times (-80)$

B. Determine each quotient.

1. $90 \div (-9)$

2. $-30 \div (-5)$

3. $-7 \div 7$

4. $81 \div (-9)$

5. $-88 \div (-8)$

6. $-48 \div 12$

7. $16 \div (-2)$

8. $24 \div (-6)$

9. $-42 \div 6$

10. $-540 \div (-9)$

11. $100 \div (-5)$

12. $-640 \div 80$

C. Determine each product or quotient.

1. $1 \times (-4)$

2. $36 \div (-9)$

3. $-10 \times (-7)$

4. $-40 \div (-5)$

5. $-45 \div 9$

6. -12×2

7. $11 \times (-3)$

8. $18 \div (-6)$

9. $-28 \div 4$

10. $-5 \times (-12)$

11. -9×8

12. $-121 \div (-11)$

Name ______________________________ Date ______________

III. Simplify Expressions Using Number Properties and the Order of Operations

A. Simplify each expression.

1. $-3 - 4(-2) + 3$

2. $(2 \div 3) \div 8$

3. $-8 + 9(-2) - 6$

4. $\frac{5}{-5}(-4)$

5. $-6 + 8 - 9(-5)$

6. $\frac{(-8 + 4)}{(-9)}$

7. $3 - 2(-6) + 9$

8. $-2(2 + 5 \cdot 3)$

9. $-3 + 7(-2 + 4)$

10. $-4(8 - 2 \cdot 2)$

11. $(-5 + 4) \div 6$

12. $-5(2 + 8 \div 2)$

B. Simplify each expression. Explain how you can use the Commutative, Associative, or Distributive Property to simplify.

1. $-10(-0.32 - 0.2)$

2. $18\frac{3}{4} + 9 - 3 + 1\frac{1}{4}$

3. $-8.17 + (8.17 + 6.54)$

4. $-3(3\frac{2}{3}) + -3(-1\frac{1}{3})$

5. $(-5\frac{2}{5} + 2\frac{1}{2}) + (-4\frac{1}{2})$

6. $(-4.2)(8.6) + (-4.2)(-4.6)$

7. $\frac{5}{12} \times (-\frac{8}{9}) \times (-\frac{12}{5})$

8. $-48.23 - 8 + 20 + 2.23$

9. $94.45 - (4.45 + 9.87)$

10. $-2(\frac{7}{2} - \frac{1}{4})$

11. $(18 - 9.9) + 12.9$

12. $-\frac{5}{8} \times 7 \times 16$

Topic 1

Algebraic Expressions

Name ______________________________ Date ______________

I. Evaluating Algebraic Expressions

A. Define a variable and write an algebraic expression for each problem. Evaluate the expression for the given values.

1. The charge for ice skating is $3 for the skate rental and $2 per hour to skate. How much will you pay if you skate for:

a. 2 hours?

b. 4 hours?

c. 3 1/2 hours?

2. A birthday party at the skating rink costs $60 to reserve a party area and $2.50 per guest for skating and skate rental. How much will a party cost if you invite:

a. 8 guests?

b. 15 guests?

c. 40 guests?

3. You have $20 to spend at the snack bar. All of the snacks at the snack bar cost $1.25. How much money will you have left if you buy:

a. 2 snacks?

b. 7 snacks?

c. 12 snacks?

4. The zamboni can resurface 1200 square feet per minute. How many minutes will it take the zamboni to resurface the entire rink if its dimensions are:

a. 80 ft × 300 ft?

b. 75 ft × 160 ft?

c. 100 ft × 210 ft?

5. The skating rink is running a promotion on skating lessons. For every twelve lessons you take, you get one free lesson. If you have already taken 7 lessons, how many free lessons will you get if you take:

a. 5 more lessons?

b. 29 more lessons?

c. 53 more lessons?

6. One lap around the skating rink is about 500 feet and the length is 175 feet. How far will you skate if you skate:

a. the length 4 times plus 10 laps?

b. the length 3 times plus 16 laps?

c. the length 6 times plus 25 laps?

7. A taxicab company charges $4.50 for each trip plus an additional $2.50 per mile traveled. How much will the company charge if the trip is:

a. 5 miles?

b. 16 miles?

c. 12.5 miles?

8. Colleen has a prepaid phone card with $40 on it. It costs her $0.09 for each minute she spends on the phone. How much money will be left on the card if Colleen speaks for:

a. 15 minutes?

b. 60 minutes?

c. 150 minutes?

9. Ty puts 9 sports cards each on the front and back page of each page in his card album. How many pages are in Ty's album if he has:

a. 90 cards?

b. 144 cards?

c. 180 cards?

10. There are 5 gallons of lemonade in a container. Sylvia fills glasses with $\frac{1}{8}$ of a gallon of lemonade from the container. How many gallons of lemonade are left in the container if Sylvia fills:

a. 7 glasses?

b. 20 glasses?

c. 32 glasses?

11. A county fair costs $8 to enter plus an additional $1.50 per ticket for rides and food. What is the total cost for a visit to the fair if you purchase:

a. 8 tickets?

b. 25 tickets?

c. 40 tickets?

12. The temperature when you got up this morning was −4 degrees Celsius. The temperature is predicted to increase by 2 degrees every hour. What will the temperature be after:

a. 2 hours?

b. 5 hours?

c. 8 hours?

Name ______________________ Date ____________

II. Multiplying and Factoring Linear Expressions

A. For each model, write the two factors that are multiplied. Then, write the product.

1.

+x +x +x +1
+1
+1
+1

2.

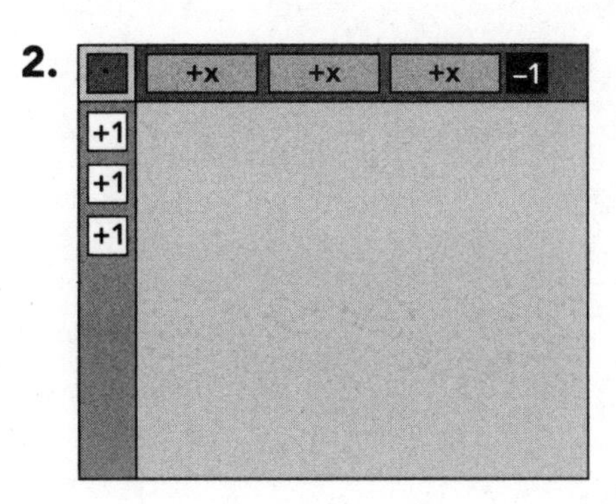

3.

–x –x –1 –1 –1
+1
+1
+1
+1

4.

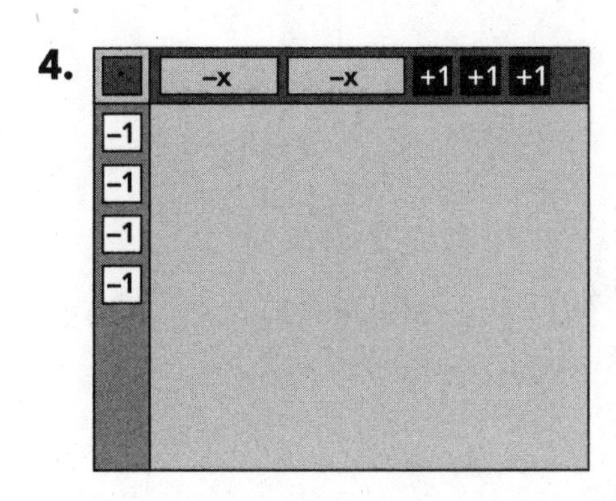

5.

+x +x +1 +1 +1
–1
–1

6.

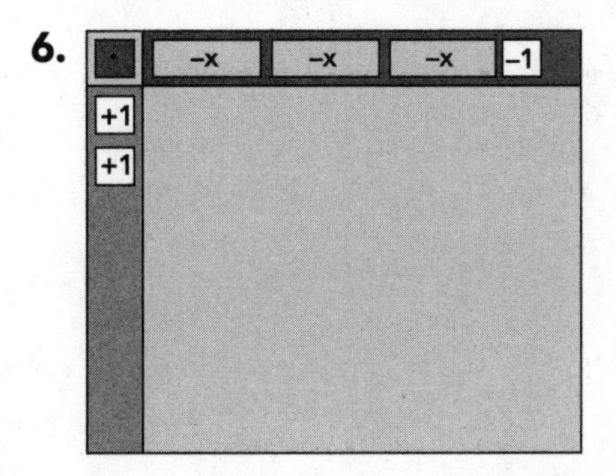

7.

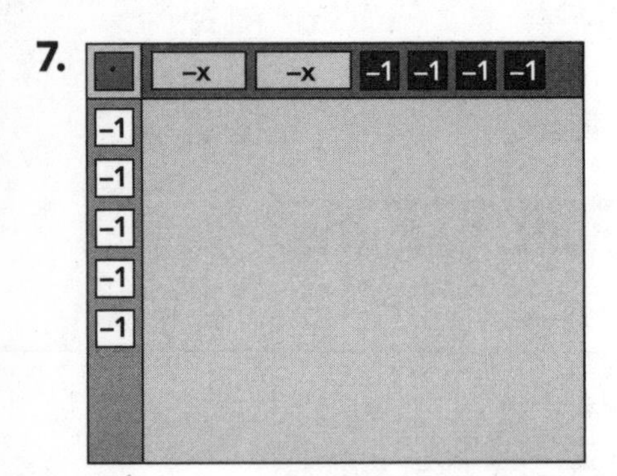
−x −x −1 −1 −1 −1
−1
−1
−1
−1
−1

8.

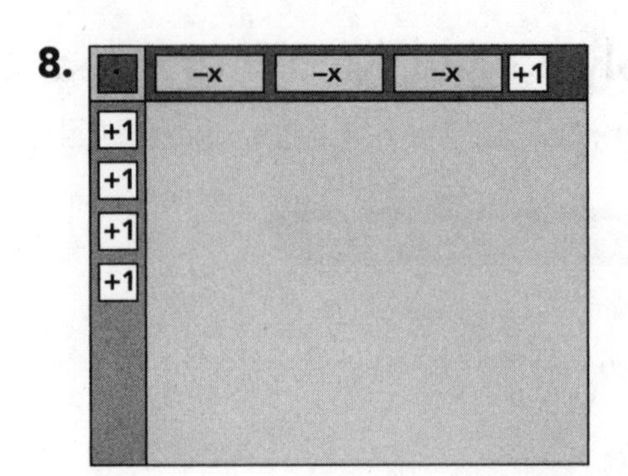
−x −x −x +1
+1
+1
+1
+1

9.

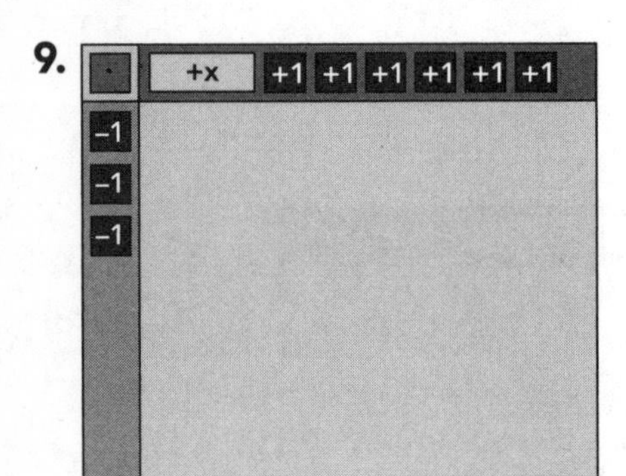
+x +1 +1 +1 +1 +1 +1
−1
−1
−1

10.

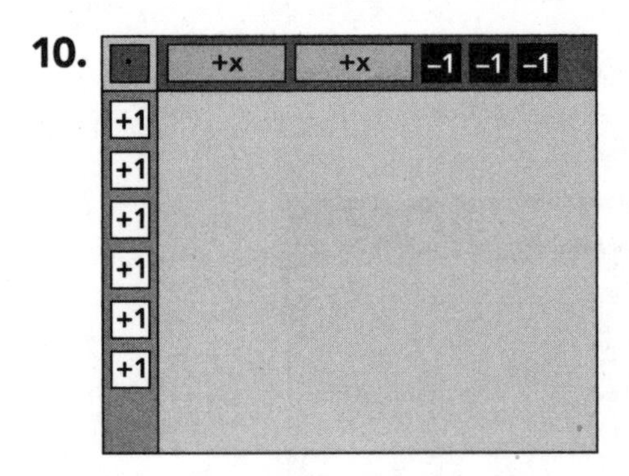
+x +x −1 −1 −1
+1
+1
+1
+1
+1
+1

11.

−x −1 −1 −1 −1 −1 −1
−1
−1
−1
−1

12.

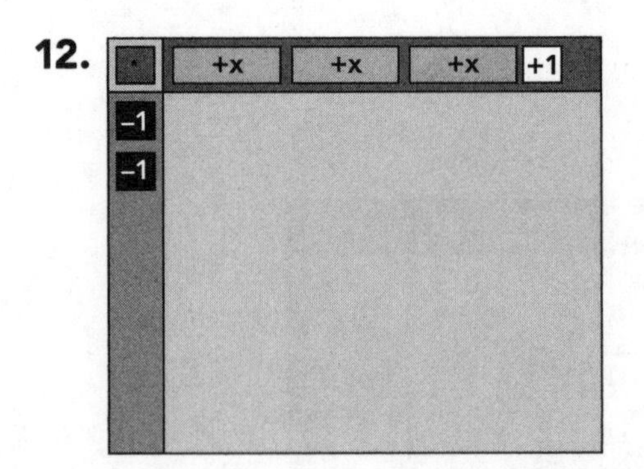
+x +x +x +1
−1
−1

Name ______________________________ Date ______________

B. Complete each statement to generate equivalent expressions.

1. $12 + 6x =$ _____ $(4 +$ _____$)$

2. $-10x - 15 =$ _____ $($_____ $+ 3)$

3. $-6 - 6x =$ _____ $(2 +$ _____$)$

4. $4x - 20 =$ _____ $($_____ $- 5)$

5. $-18 - 12x =$ _____ $(3 +$ _____$)$

6. $-24x + 15 =$ _____ $($_____ $- 5)$

7. $24 + 64x =$ _____ $(3 +$ _____$)$

8. $54x - 81 =$ _____ $($_____ $- 3)$

9. $-5x - 35 =$ _____ $($_____ $+ 7)$

10. $36 - 8x =$ _____ $(9 -$ _____$)$

11. $-60x + 35 =$ _____ $($_____ $- 7)$

12. $33 - 3x =$ _____ $(11 -$ _____$)$

III. Simplifying Algebraic Expressions

A. Simplify each expression completely by combining like terms, using number properties, and using the Order of Operations.

1. $-4x - 4 \div 9$

2. $2 - (4(-2)x \div -2)$

3. $-3 + 1(-6)x - 7x$

4. $-2x + 9x \cdot 7 + 36$

5. $5x + (6x \div -9)$

6. $-2x(8 + 3 \cdot 4)$

7. $-3x \cdot 9 + 4 \div 4 - 8$

8. $5x + 8(-8x - 3)$

9. $5x - 3x \cdot 3 - 25$

10. $3x + 8x(-6 + 1)$

11. $-2x(-25) - 3 \div 2^2 + 1$

12. $9x - \frac{9 \cdot 6x}{18}$

Topic 2

Two-Step Equations and Inequalities

Name ______________________________ Date ______________

I. Modeling Two-Step Expressions and Equations

A. Create a bar model to represent each situation. Use the model to help you write an equation and solve the problem.

1. Eva and Dulcina have 82 pins together. Dulcina has 34 more pins than Eva. How many pins are in Dulcina's collection? How many pins are in Eva's collection?

2. Put together, Albert and Jason have 110 total action figures. Jason's collection has 42 more action figures in it than Albert's collection. How many action figures does Jason have? How many action figures are in Albert's collection?

3. Tripp and Rico are two dogs. Tripp weighs exactly 35 pounds more than Rico. Together, they weigh exactly 49 pounds. How much does each dog weigh?

4. Enrique's collection has 64 fewer refrigerator magnets in it than Peter's collection. They have 112 refrigerator magnets together. How many refrigerator magnets does Enrique have? How many refrigerator magnets does Peter have?

Name ______________________________ Date ______________

5. Anna buys bananas, grapes, and apples. She buys twice the amount of bananas as grapes. She buys 2 more pounds of apples than grapes. Altogether, Anna bought 14 pounds of fruit. How many pounds of each fruit did she buy?

6. You and your friends Kyra and Paolo decide to make some money during summer vacation by building and selling birdhouses. To get the business started, Kyra contributes $22, and Paolo contributes $18 to buy equipment and materials. You all agree that each person will earn the same amount of money after Kyra and Paolo get back what they invested. Your business earns a total of $280. How much does each person get at the end of the summer?

7. In a small town, there are two main sections called the Hill Section and the Lake Section. The town has a population of 4298. The number of people who live in the Hill Section is 188 more than twice the number of people who live in the Lake Section. How many people live in each section of the town?

8. Tanner is 3 years younger than his sister, Lexi. The sum of the siblings' ages is 33. How old are Tanner and Lexi?

9. The members of the student council are selling raffle tickets. The school decides that the top three raffle ticket sellers will share a portion of the profits. The second-place seller will receive $8 more than the third-place seller. The first-place seller will receive twice as much as the second-place seller. The profit portion they will share is $104. How much will each of the top three sellers receive?

10. The ages of three siblings total 32 years. The middle child is 4 years older than the youngest, and the eldest is twice as old as the youngest. How old is each child?

11. Two friends pooled the tickets they won from playing video games to get a prize that requires 800 tickets. If one friend won 130 more tickets than the other friend, how many tickets did each friend win?

12. Of the 3120 books in the library, there are three times as many books in the fiction section as are in the nonfiction section. Also, there are 400 fewer books in the reference section than are in the nonfiction section. How many books are in each section?

Name ______________________________ Date ______________

13. Cameron, Hannah, and Daniel are swimming laps to raise money for charity. Together, the three swimmers swam a total of 1875 laps. Hannah swam twice as many laps as Daniel. Cameron swam 125 more laps than Hannah. How many laps did each person swim?

14. During the summer, Curran and AJ started their own business mowing lawns. Before starting any work, Curran spent $20 to fill up the gas tank for the lawnmower. The boys agreed that each person would earn the same amount after Curran was reimbursed the money he spent for gas. After a week of work, the boys were paid a total of $177. Curran filled up the gas tank just once. How much did each boy earn?

15. A park covers a total area of 644 acres. There are 482 more acres of woods than grassy areas in the park. How many acres are there of woods and how many acres are there of grassy areas in the park?

16. There are 7800 workers in the three main buildings downtown. Three hundred fewer people work in the second-largest building than the largest building and 900 fewer people work in the smallest building than the largest building. How many workers are in each building?

PAGE 68

B. Solve each equation using a double number line.

1. Solve the equation $2x + 8 = 20$.

2. Solve the equation $3t + 15 = 45$.

3. Solve the equation $23 = 4d + 5$.

4. Solve the equation $\frac{1}{4}x + 2 = 10$.

5. Solve the equation $31.8 = 5w - 6.7$.

6. Solve the equation $3(b + 2) = 21$.

7. Solve the equation $6m + 7.2 = -2.8$.

8. Solve the equation $\frac{1}{3}x - 1 = 11$.

9. Solve the equation $6(c - 3) = 2$.

10. Solve the equation $2y - 4.25 = -1.39$.

Name ______________________________ Date ______________

11. Solve the equation $3n - 3\frac{1}{4} = -6$.

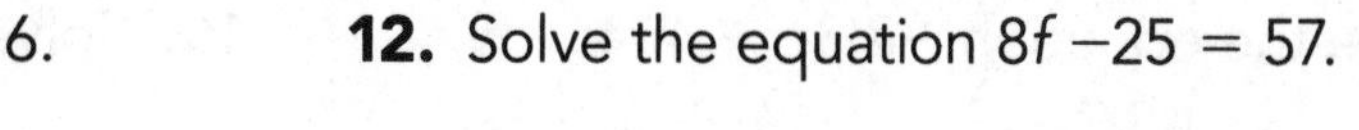

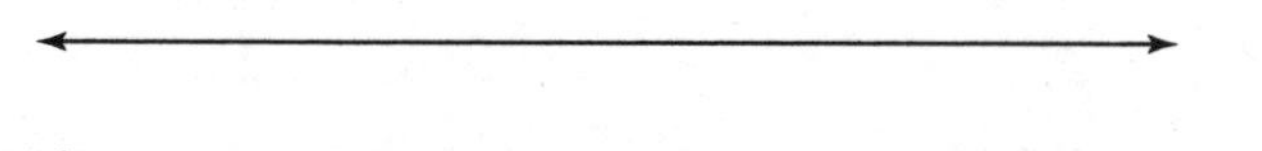

12. Solve the equation $8f - 25 = 57$.

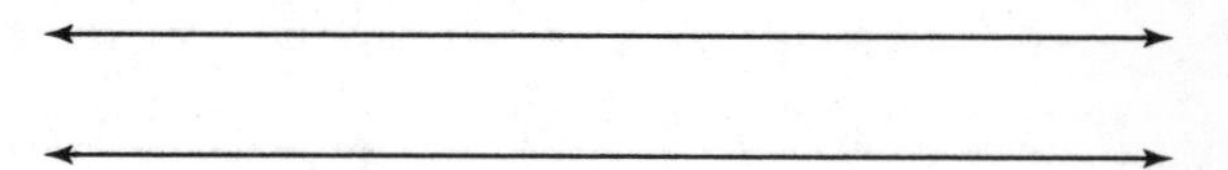

C. Solve each equation using a double number line.

1. Solve the equation $-2(2x + 2) = 8$.

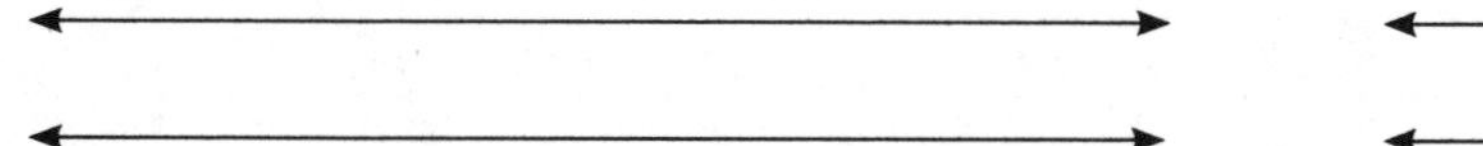

2. Solve the equation $-b + 12 = 30$.

3. Solve the equation $-\frac{1}{2}m - 3 = 10$.

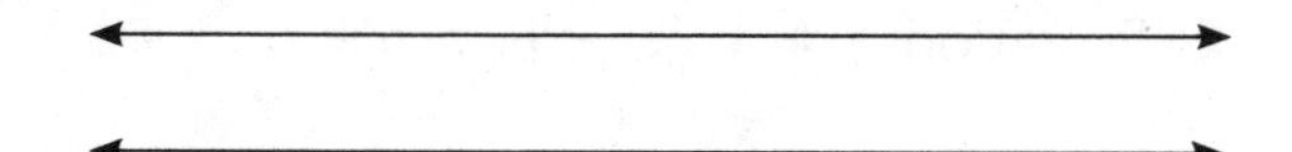

4. Solve the equation $-4y + 9 = 27$.

5. Solve the equation $-4(a - 1) = 36$.

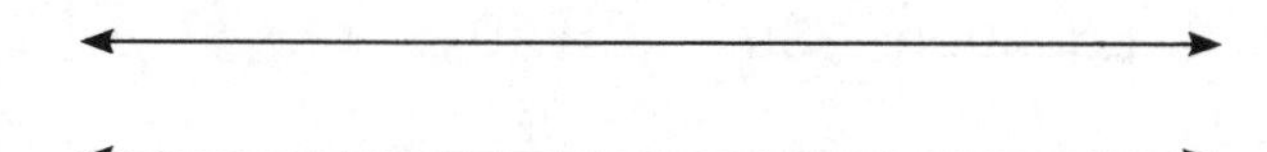

6. Solve the equation $-7x - 11 = -4$.

7. Solve the equation $-1.2s + 6.4 = 8.8$.

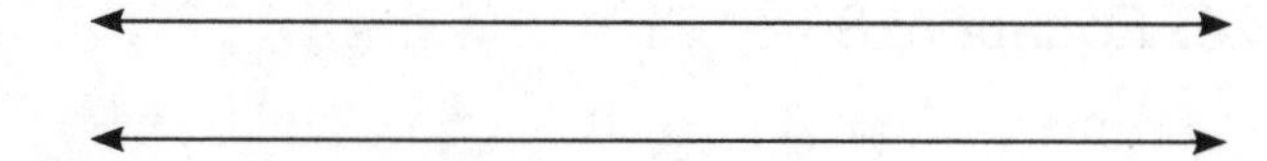

8. Solve the equation $-16 = 13 - g$.

9. Solve the equation $-3(3c + 4) = -9$.

10. Solve the equation $41 = -9k - 4$.

11. Solve the equation $200 - \frac{1}{4}p = 215$.

12. Solve the equation $-50x + 70 = 80$.

II. Solving Two-Step Equations

A. Determine whether each solution is a solution to the given equation.

1. Equation: $\frac{c}{2} + 5 = 2$

Solution: $c = -6$

2. Equation: $-4 = 2p + 8$

Solution: $p = -1$

3. Equation: $2p - 4 = 8$

Solution: $p = -3$

4. Equation: $-3u - 8 = 10$

Solution: $u = -6$

5. Equation: $10 = 3n - 5$

Solution: $n = -4$

6. Equation: $8 = \frac{z}{-3} + 4$

Solution: $z = -12$

PAGE 71

Name ______________________ Date ______________

7. Equation: $-2m - 10 = 4$

Solution: $m = -2$

8. Equation: $7 = \frac{h}{9} - 4$

Solution: $h = -9$

9. Equation: $-9w + 4 = 4$

Solution: $w = 0$

10. Equation: $-9 = \frac{r}{3} - 4$

Solution: $r = -15$

11. Equation: $3z - 9 = -6$

Solution: $z = 9$

12. Equation: $-7 = \frac{b}{-2} - 2$

Solution: $b = 10$

B. Solve each equation for the variable.

1. Solve for z: $-2 + 10z = 28$.

2. Solve for a: $\frac{a}{-9} - 10 = 8$.

3. Solve for w: $-11 = 9 + 10w$.

4. Solve for x: $-10 = -5x + 5$.

5. Solve for *s*: $2 + \frac{s}{7} = 2$.

6. Solve for *n*: $\frac{n}{8} - 10 = -11$.

7. Solve for *b*: $-12 = 4b + 4$.

8. Solve for *p*: $5 + \frac{p}{3} = 6$.

9. Solve for *y*: $7 = -7 - y$.

10. Solve for *x*: $4 = \frac{x}{3} - 1$.

11. Solve for *c*: $2 = -c - 6$.

12. Solve for *w*: $10 = 10 - 4w$.

13. Solve for *k*: $4 = -2 + (\frac{k}{-5})$.

14. Solve for *z*: $-4 = \frac{z}{5} - 7$.

15. Solve for *y*: $-7 = 3 + 2y$.

16. Solve for *u*: $5 + (\frac{u}{-2}) = 1$

Name ________________________________ Date ________________

17. Solve for g: $-28 = 9g - 10$.

18. Solve for j: $-16 = -10 + \frac{j}{2}$.

19. Solve for t: $\frac{t}{9} + 9 = 8$.

20. Solve for z: $25 = 5 + 5z$.

21. Solve for m: $-9 = -6m + 3$.

22. Solve for v: $2 = \frac{v}{-10} + 4$.

23. Solve for x: $4x + 3 = 1$.

24. Solve for d: $-9 = \frac{d}{-6} + 7$.

C. Solve each equation.

1. $-8 = 2 - 4y$

2. $1 = -6w - 2$

3. $8 = 7 + (\frac{w}{-4})$

4. $-12 = \frac{z}{6} - 10$

5. $10 = 9 + 5w$

6. $7 = 8 + (\frac{x}{-8})$

7. $-3w + 1 = 0$

8. $4 = \frac{y}{3} + 3$

9. $1 + 9y = -44$

10. $5 = 10 + \frac{y}{6}$

11. $\frac{w}{-10} + 6 = -1$

12. $-3x + 4 = 13$

D. Solve each literal equation for the given variable.

1. Solve $d = rt$ for t.

2. Solve $A = \frac{1}{2}bh$ for h.

3. Solve $Q = \frac{c + d}{2}$ for d.

4. Solve $y = mx + b$ for x.

5. Solve $A = \frac{\pi r^2 S}{360}$ for S.

6. Solve $S = ut + \frac{1}{2}at^2$ for a.

Name ______________________________ Date ______________

III. Solving Two-Step Inequalities

A. Represent each inequality on the number line.

1. $x < 2$

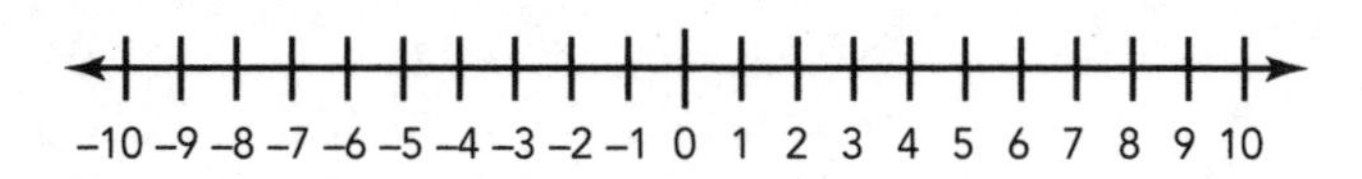

2. $-5 \geq x$

3. $\frac{1}{2} < x$

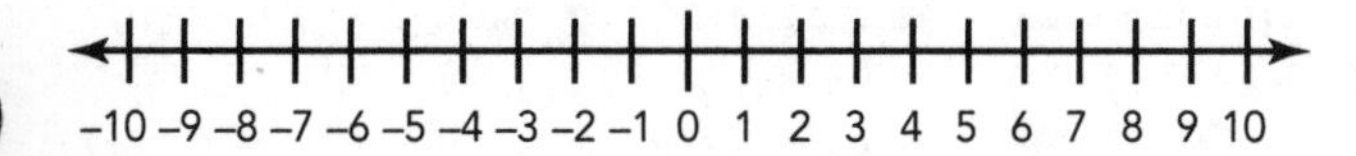

4. $x \geq -3.8$

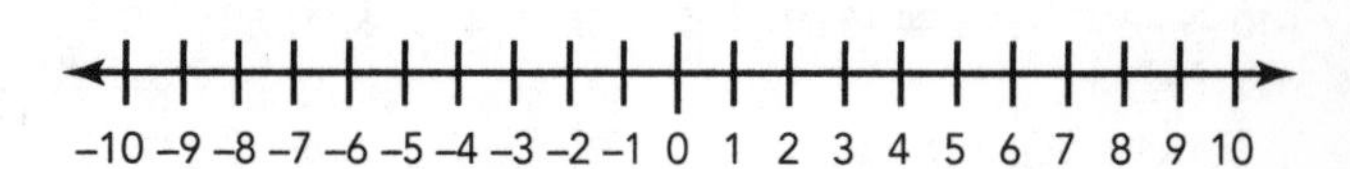

5. $-4 < x$

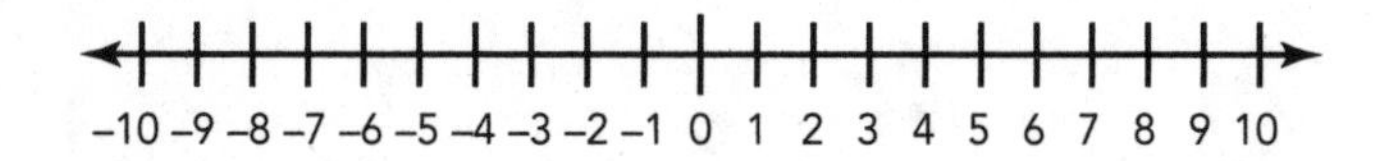

6. $x \leq -7\frac{1}{3}$

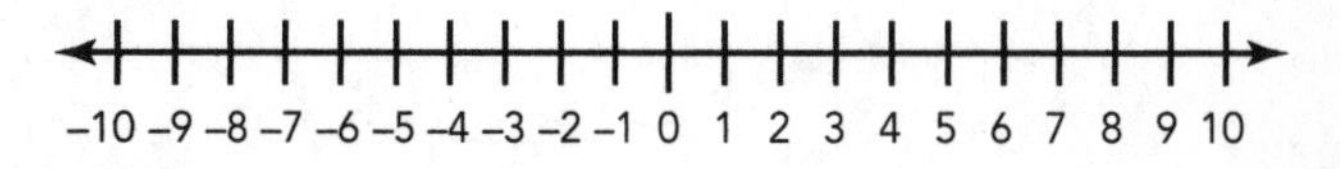

7. $3 \geq x$

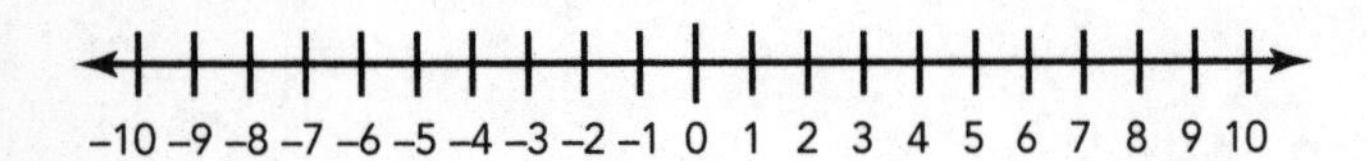

8. $x \leq -9$

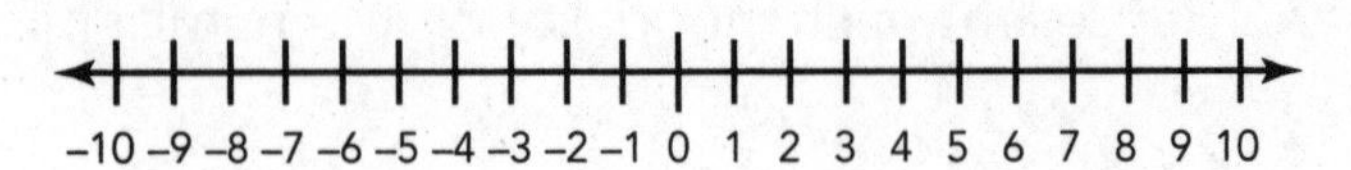

9. $x < 6\frac{5}{8}$

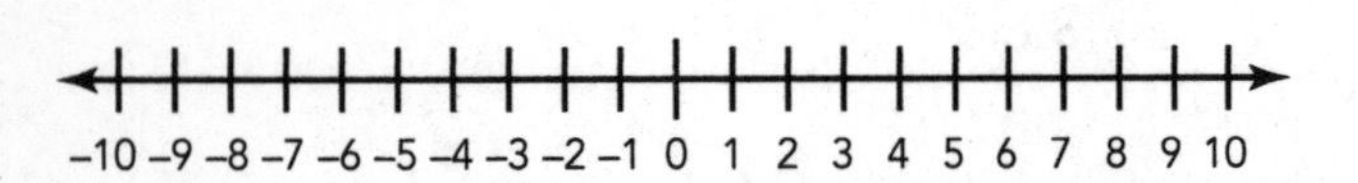

10. $-0.8 < x$

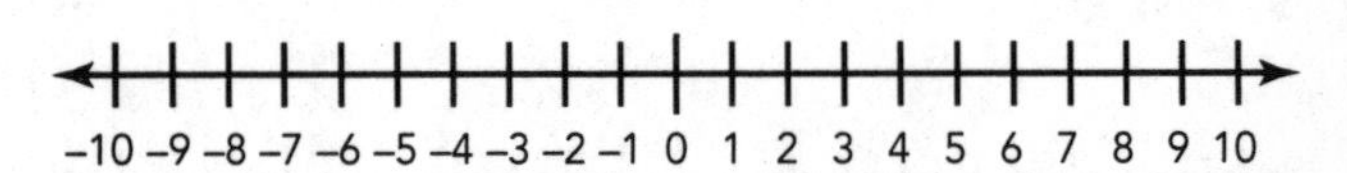

B. Solve each inequality.

1. $-4x + 39 \geq -29$

2. $-3x + 37 \geq 55$

3. $-8x - 27 < 5$

4. $28 \leq 5x + 18$

Name ____________________ Date ____________

5. $59 > 2x + 45$

6. $-x - 4 \leq -11$

7. $6x + 11 < -31$

8. $-15 > -2x - 19$

9. $-2x - 29 \leq -55$

10. $-52 \geq 8x + 44$

11. $62 > -5x + 27$

12. $2x - 23 < -29$

Topic 3

Multiple Representations of Equations

Name ______________________________ Date ______________

I. Problem Solving with Two-Step Equations and Inequalities

A. Identify the independent and dependent quantity in each scenario.

1. A forest fire can move at the rate of three meters per second in windy conditions. A fire started by a careless camper has already moved 45 meters.

2. Andrea's dog sleeps 9 hours at night and then takes several 2-hour naps during the daytime.

3. The cooking club sells stickers featuring Featherbrain the Turkey, the school's mascot. In one hour, they sell $28 worth of stickers. Each member who sells stickers is paid $1.

4. The music club takes polls each year about the popularity of musicians. Jazzy Joe's popularity peaked when he scored 20 points in the poll. Since then, his score has dropped 2 points every year.

5. For the school's Track and Field Day, every class participated in the egg-in-spoon relay race. The eighth grade class started 14 meters behind the starting line to eliminate their age advantage, and the class walked at a rate of 2 meters per second.

6. You want to track your net savings from using a particular rechargeable battery. The rechargeable battery costs $19 more than a similar disposable battery, which costs $4. That means for every recharging of the battery, you save $4 that you would otherwise have spent on a new disposable battery.

Name ______________________________ Date ______________

7. Consuelo is a spelunker, a person who explores caves for sport. To get to the entrance of her favorite cave, she crawls down three feet. Then, once in the cave, she continues to descend at a rate of about six feet per minute.

8. Jessica's free-range worm farm consistently brought in $25 a week, so it wasn't long before she paid her mom back the $31 she owed her mom for start-up costs. She stashed away the rest of her money.

9. The traffic fine for speeding in a school zone in one town is $50 plus $9 for every mile per hour above the speed limit that the driver is traveling. Francis is pulled over for speeding in a school zone.

10. Maya owes her sister $85. Each week she pays off $2 of the debt to her sister.

11. Alyssa buys a $15 club membership in order to get nail pens for $6 each.

12. A professional football team has advanced 3 yards from the half line towards their opponent's goal line. They're doing well, but then they receive a series of penalties. Each penalty moves the team backwards 5 yards and farther away from their opponent's goal line.

B. Solve each problem.

1. Yolanda's Flower Shop sells long-stem roses for $5 each. In addition, the shop charges a $15 shipping fee. How many roses can Santo purchase if he plans to spend $90?

2. Sylvia is practicing for her next track meet by running laps and recording her time. For each timed practice run, Sylvia runs a total of 2000 meters. Each lap is exactly 200 meters. If Sylvia has exactly 200 meters left to run, how many laps has she completed?

3. Greg buys 40 yards of wire fence to create a triangular pen for his dog. One side of the pen will use 19 yards of fencing. The other two sides will be equal in length. Greg would like his pen to use exactly 40 yards of fencing so that he doesn't have any left over. What is the length of each of the other two sides of the pen?

4. Your cable bill this month was exactly $105. The regular fee for cable is $97, but this month you rented 2 movies that each cost the same amount to rent. How much did each movie cost to rent?

5. Since beginning his artistic career, Cameron has painted 6 paintings a year. He has sold all but two of his paintings. If Cameron has sold 70 paintings, how many years has he been painting?

6. At the dance recital, Ms. Deutsch needs seven parent volunteers to help students get on and off stage, plus four parent volunteers per room of students. On the day of the recital, Ms. Deutsch uses 39 parent volunteers. How many backstage rooms were there?

Name ____ Date ____________________

7. After his alarm rings, Clarence has 25 minutes to get ready. He snoozes in bed for one minute after the alarm rings the first day, two minutes the second day, three minutes the third day, etc. When Clarence is down to 11 minutes to get ready, how many days has it been?

8. The student council started the year with a balance of −$15 (they were in debt), but after they came up with the idea to sell tickets to a student vs. faculty mud fight, the fund grew by $15 a minute. By the time the student council had a balance of $90, how long had they been selling tickets?

9. A sculptor used 12 bars to make the first cube of a sculpture. To make each additional cube, the sculptor attached 8 bars to the previous cube. How many additional cubes were in the sculpture if the sculptor used 44 bars?

10. The Bagel Club at Middle Township High School sells bagels to teachers for $2 each. Each day they spend $!9 on supplies. How many bagels did the club sell on Thursday if their profit was $55?

11. Suppose you are given a ten-yard head start in a race with a friend. Each second from the start of the race, your friend gains one yard on you. How many seconds does it take for your friend to catch up to you?

12. The North Colony Trail at Royal Gorge, Colorado, is 18 miles long. Stacey has hiked eight miles to a resting spot. She hikes the rest of the trail at two miles per hour. When Stacey reached the sixteenth mile, how long has she been walking from the resting spot?

C. Solve each problem.

1. Arthur is creating a garden in his backyard. He has less than 250 square yards of space to use. He plans to use 25 square yards to plant flowers. He plans to divide the remaining space into plots of equal size for vegetables. Each vegetable plot will be 30 square yards. How many plots of equal size can Arthur plan for vegetables?

2. Diana is practicing her pitching. She rotates pitching from the mound with the other pitchers on the team. Diana throws 20 pitches each time she rotates to the mound. Her coach said she must throw more than 400 pitches in the strike zone during today's practice. How many rotations must Diana take if a total of 20 of her pitches miss the strike zone?

3. The principal of Gates High School promised that the school will provide busing for more than 70 students to the homecoming game. The 9 senior athletes are taking part in a special awards ceremony, so the principal rents a large van to bring them to the game. He rents large buses for all of the other students. Each bus holds 25 students. How many buses will the principal need to rent to keep his promise?

4. Takira is setting up for a cat show. The convention center has set aside 350 square yards of space for the show. The fire code says there must be more than 40 square yards of free space for the walkway in the show. Takira is planning for each exhibit to take up 40 square yards of space. How many exhibits can Takira have in the show?

Name ______________________________ Date ______________

5. Seiki is planning her workout at her gym. She wants to spend more than 40 minutes exercising. Her workout plan includes 20 minutes lifting weights and the rest of the time on 3 different cardio machines. She wants to spend the same amount of time on each cardio machine. How many minutes should Seiki spend on each cardio machine?

6. You and 4 friends are starting a business selling bagels. The 5 of you open a bank account strictly for the business. You would like to have at least $70 in the account after you buy the start-up supplies. You all estimate that the start-up supplies will cost $25 and decide that each person must deposit the same whole-dollar amount of money into the account. How much money should each person deposit into the account so that you have at least $70 after buying start-up supplies?

7. Ms. Chu is in charge of the school music assembly. The assembly is 100 minutes in length and contains music from 3 different ensembles. She would like less than 13 minutes of "down time" during the assembly, which includes the time it takes the ensembles to get on and off the stage. Each ensemble will have the same whole-number amount of time, in minutes, to perform. How many minutes should Ms. Chu allow for each ensemble?

8. Vondra read that she should have less than 15 fish based upon the size of her fish tank. She already has 4 tetras in her tank. She would like to add 2 new types of fish to her tank. She would like the same number of each new type of fish. How many of each new type of fish can Vondra add to her tank?

9. In a game against the Creek Side Crickets, the East Port Pandas football team score one touchdown with an extra point, which gave them 7 points. Their kicker made every field goal he attempted for 3 points each. The Panda's final score was less than the Crickets' score, which was 23 points. How many field goals did the Pandas make?

10. A car dealership must sell at least 60 cars per week to fulfill their quota. The owner, Ms. Maruti, knows that she personally will sell 9 cars per week. She has 10 other salespeople that each work at her dealership. If each of Ms. Maruti's salespeople sells the same number of cars, how many must each of them sell each week to meet the dealership's quota?

11. Faith makes fresh tacos each day to be shipped and sold in local grocery stores. She packages the tacos in collectible lunch pails. Each taco weighs 5 ounces. Each lunch pail weighs 14 ounces. Due to shipping regulations, the total weight of each taco lunch pail can be, at most, 40 ounces. How many tacos can Faith package in each lunch pail?

12. Deven is a graphic artist. He is saving files on a USB drive to give to a client. The USB drive can hold at most 200 megabytes of data. Deven has one high resolution file already on the USB drive. It is 50 megabytes. Deven wants to add some low resolution files to the USB drive. Each low resolution file is 6 megabytes. How many low resolution files can Deven add to the USB drive?

Name ______________________________ Date ______________

II. Graphs of Equations

A. Solve each problem.

1. The library charges $1 to use the copier and $0.50 for each page copied. Complete the table. Then use the table to graph the relationship.

Number of Pages	Total Cost (dollars)
2	
	6
15	
	10

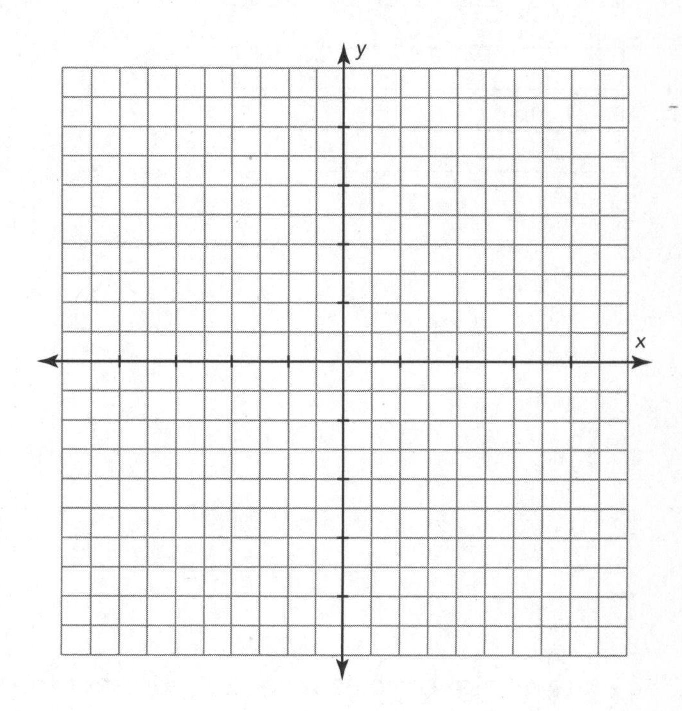

Write an algebraic equation to represent the situation.

a. How many pages were copied if the total cost was $7.50?

b. What is the total cost to copy 50 pages?

2. The bakery charges $7.50 for one dozen bagels and $0.50 for each additional bagel. Complete the table. Then use the table to graph the relationship.

Number of Bagels	Total Cost (dollars)
12	
	8.00
15	
	9.50

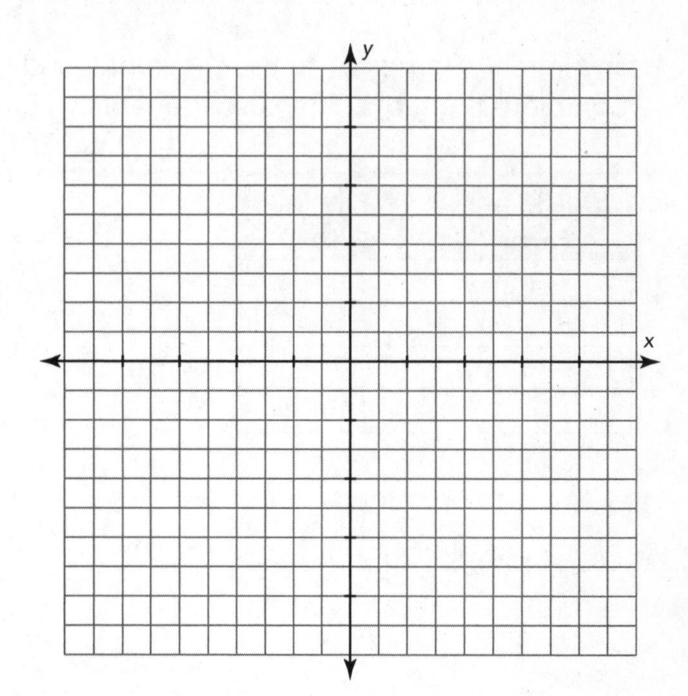

Write an algebraic equation to represent the situation.

a. How much will 2 dozen bagels cost?

b. How many bagels can you buy for $20?

Name ______________________________ Date ______________

3. At a local farm it costs $5 to pick your own peck of apples. It costs $3 for each additional peck. Complete the table. Then use the table to graph the relationship.

Number of Pecks	Total Cost (dollars)
	5
	11
4	
6	

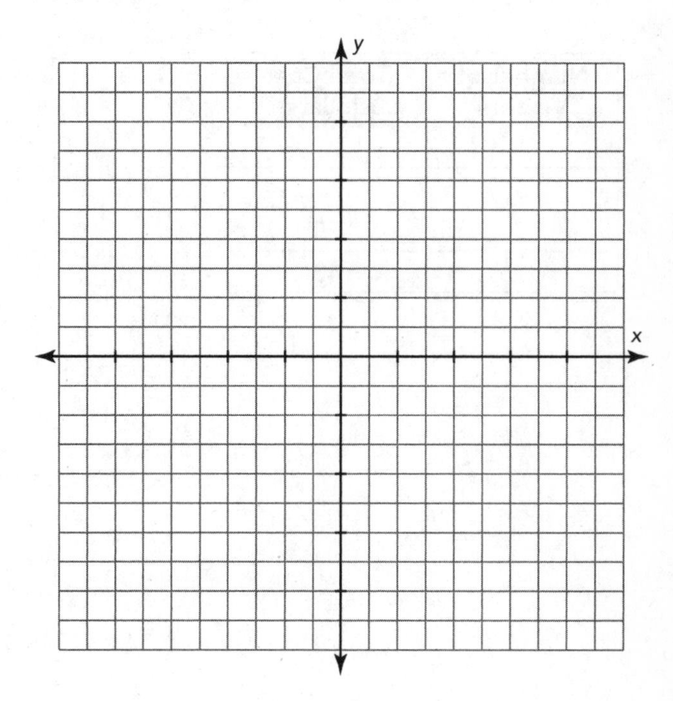

Write an algebraic equation to represent the situation.

a. How much will 11 pecks of apples cost?

b. How many pecks can you buy for $17?

4. A children's museum charges $10 admission for the first visitor and $5 for each additional visitor in a group. Complete the table. Then use the table to graph the relationship.

Number of Visitors	Total Cost (dollars)
1	
3	
	25
	40

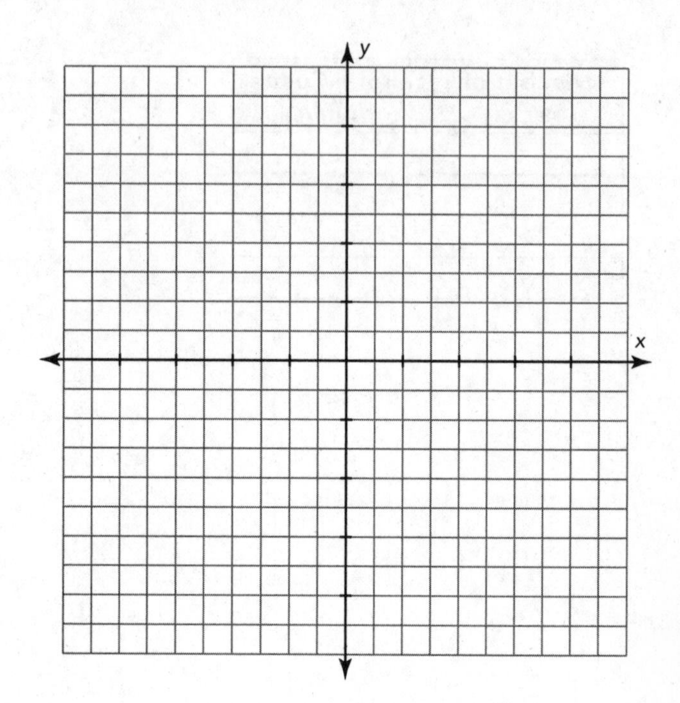

Write an algebraic equation to represent the situation.

a. How much will a group of 14 visitors cost?

b. How many visitors are in a group if the admission cost for the group is $50?

Name ______________________________ Date ______________

5. A party store charges $18 for 6 foil balloons and $2 for each additional foil balloon. Complete the table. Then use the table to graph the relationship.

Number of Balloons	Total Cost (dollars)
	18
7	
8	
	26

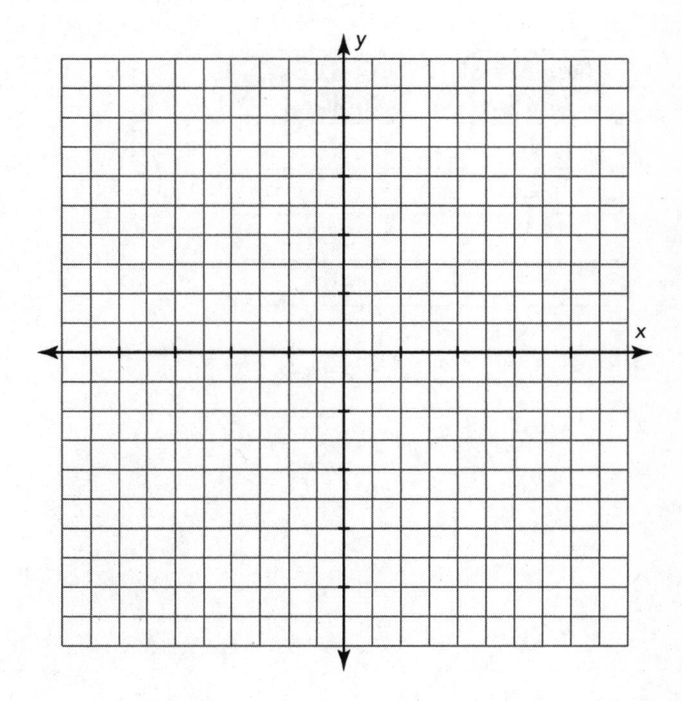

Write an algebraic equation to represent the situation.

a. What is the total cost for 16 balloons?

b. How many balloons can you buy for $50?

6. The bakery charges $4.50 for one dozen muffins and $0.25 for each additional muffin. Complete the table. Then use the table to graph the relationship.

Number of Muffins	Total Cost (dollars)
12	
13	
	5.50
	6

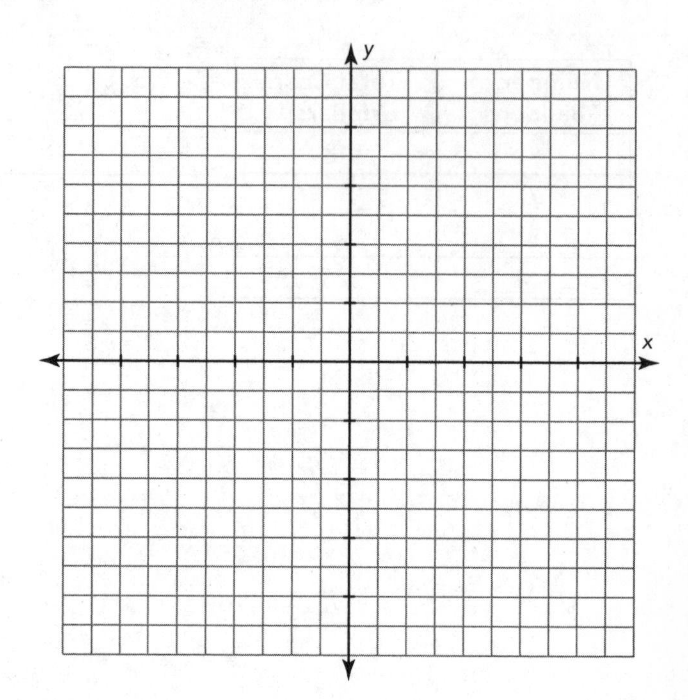

Write an algebraic equation to represent the situation.

a. How many muffins can you buy for $12?

b. What do 24 muffins cost?

Name ______________________________ Date ______________

7. A submarine is diving at a rate of 0.25 meter per second. Complete the table. Then use the table to graph the relationship.

Time (seconds)	Depth (meters)
8	
30	
	−9.25
	−10

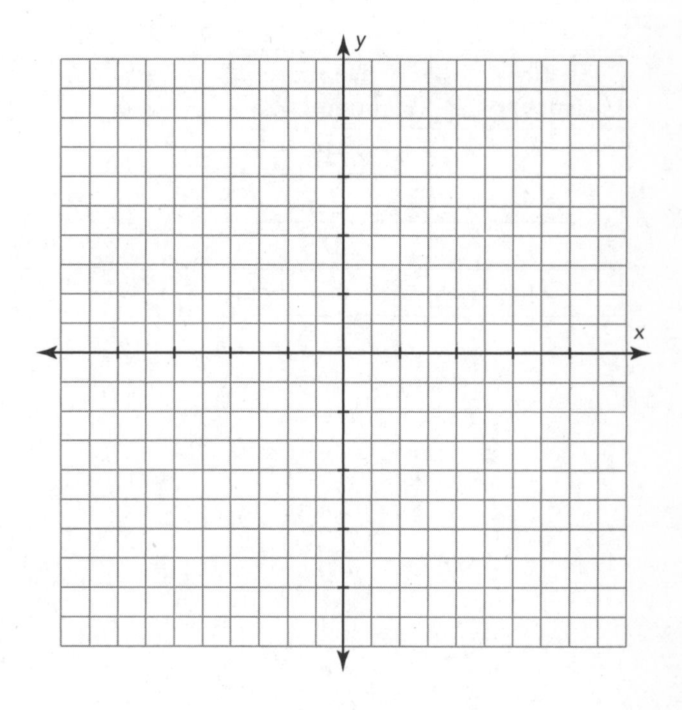

Write an algebraic equation to represent the situation.

a. What is the submarine's depth after 24 seconds?

b. After how many seconds will the submarine be at a depth of −50 meters?

PAGE 92

8. A submarine starts at a depth of −15 meters and then dives down 0.5 meter every second. Complete the table. Then use the table to graph the relationship.

Time (seconds)	Depth (meters)
	−15
1	
	−17.5
10	

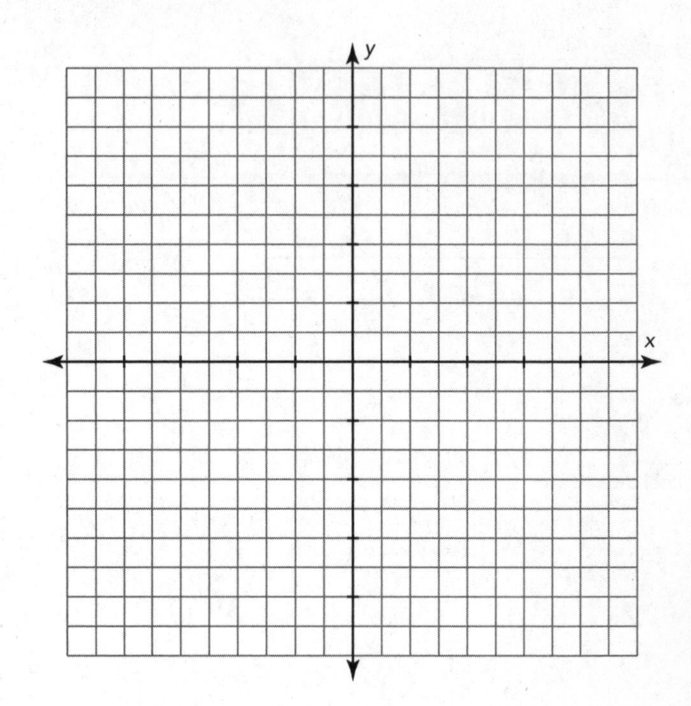

Write an algebraic equation to represent the situation.

a. How deep will the submarine be after 25 seconds?

b. After how many seconds will the submarine be at a depth of −30 meters?

Name ______________________________ Date ______________

9. A helicopter starts at a height of 50 meters and rises 12.5 meters every second. Complete the table. Then use the table to graph the relationship.

Time (seconds)	Height (meters)
	50
	75
6	
9	

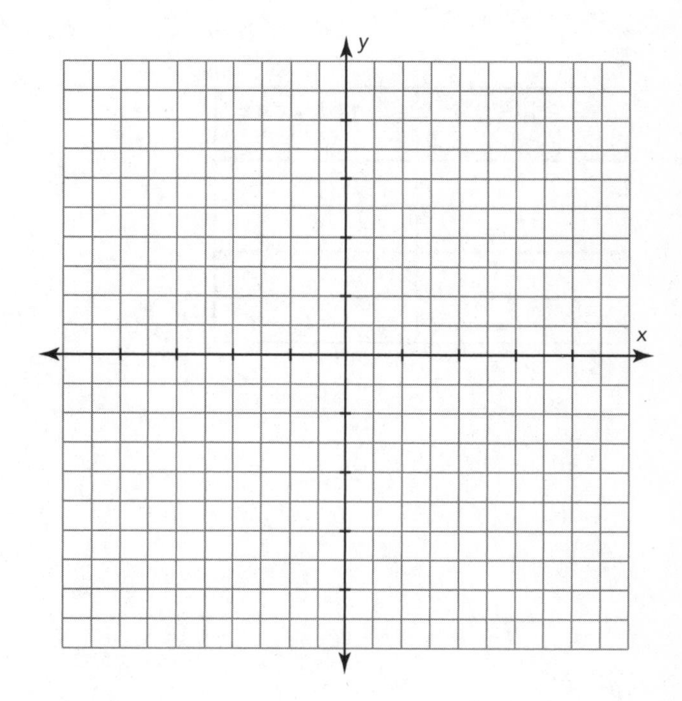

Write an algebraic equation to represent the situation.

a. After how many seconds will the helicopter be at a height of 100 meters?

b. At what height will the helicopter be after 15 seconds?

10. At noon, the temperature was 92 degrees Fahrenheit. The temperature dropped 5 degrees every hour after that. Complete the table. Then use the table to graph the relationship.

Time (hours)	Temperature (°F)
2	
5	
	42
	27

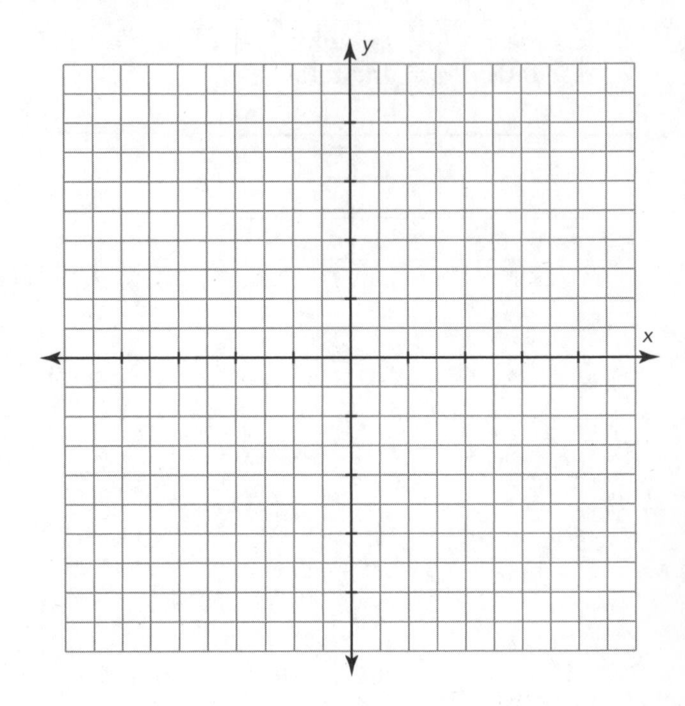

Write an algebraic equation to represent the situation.

a. After how many hours will the temperature be 74°F?

b. What will the temperature be in 8 hours?

Name ______________________________ Date ______________

11. Raul is considering a new internet service provider. He has been using his current provider for 4 months and has already paid $160 for the service. His bills average $40 per month. Complete the table. Then use the table to graph the relationship.

Time (months)	Total Cost (dollars)
–1	
	160
	200
2	

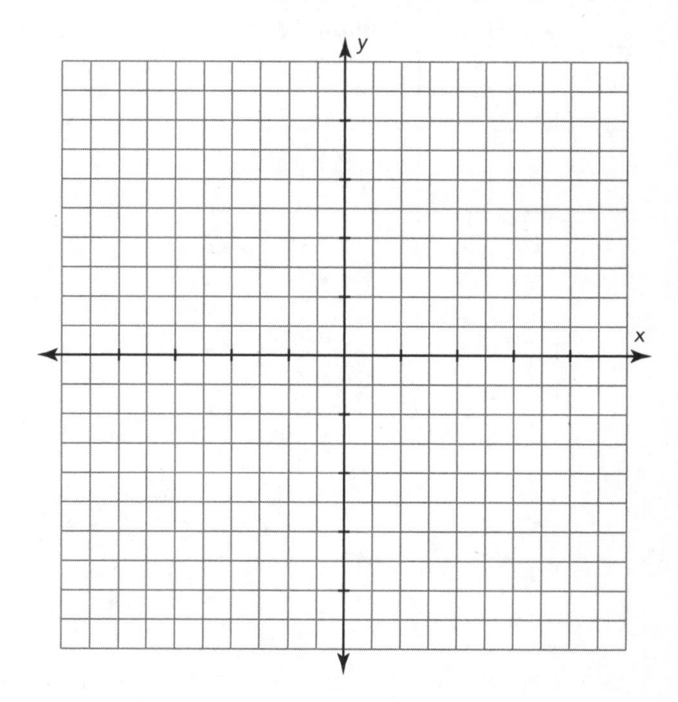

Write an algebraic equation to represent the situation.

a. When did the cost of Raul's internet service exceed $100?

b. What had Raul's internet service cost 3 months ago?

12. Right now, Miguel is 9 kilometers into a 36-kilometer race. He is running an average of 18 kilometers every hour. Complete the table. Then use the table to graph the relationship.

Time (hour)	Distance (kilometers)
	9
0.5	
	22.5
1	

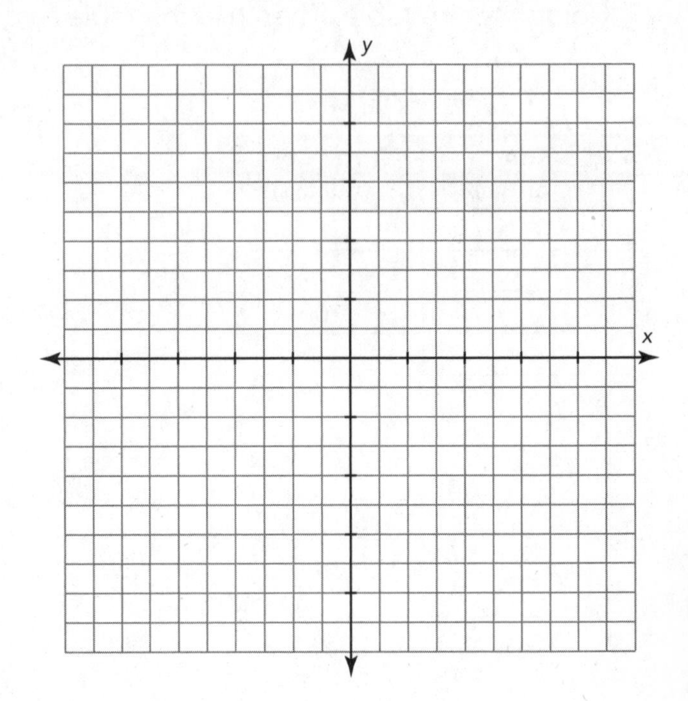

Write an algebraic equation to represent the situation.

a. How many kilometers of the race had Miguel completed half an hour ago?

b. How much longer will it take Miguel to complete the race?

Name ______________________________ Date ______________

III. Using Tables to Write Equations

A. Write an equation that represents each problem situation.

1. The table shows the total cost for dinner in the banquet room of Anthony's Bistro.

Number of Guests	Total Cost
	Anthony's Bistro
10	\$169.90
11	\$185.89
12	\$201.88
13	\$217.87
14	\$233.86
15	\$249.85

Write an equation that represents the total cost for dinner at Anthony's Bistro, t, in terms of the number of guests, g.

2. The table shows the total cost for dinner in the banquet room of Emilio's Ristorante.

Number of Guests	Total Cost
	Emilio's Ristorante
10	\$214.90
11	\$227.89
12	\$240.88
13	\$253.87
14	\$266.86
15	\$279.85

Write an equation that represents the total cost for dinner at Emilio's Ristorante, t, in terms of the number of guests, g.

3. The table shows the total cost of admission for large groups to Ocean World.

Number of Students	Total Cost
	Ocean World
20	\$330.00
21	\$341.50
22	\$353.00
23	\$364.50
24	\$376.00

Write an equation that represents the total cost of admission to Ocean World, t, in terms of the number of students, s.

4. The table shows the total cost of admission for large groups to Safari Land.

Number of Students	Total Cost
	Safari Land
20	\$370.00
21	\$379.50
22	\$389.00
23	\$398.50
24	\$408.00

Write an equation that represents the total cost of admission to Safari Land, t, in terms of the number of students, s.

PAGE 98

5. The Gladiolus plants at the garden center are 4 inches tall and grow at a rate of 3 inches per week. Write an equation that represents the height of the Gladiolus plants, *h*, in terms of the number of weeks, *w*.

6. The Dahlia plants at the garden center are 6 inches tall and grow at a rate of 2.5 inches per week. Write an equation that represents the height of the Dahlia plants, *h*, in terms of the number of weeks, *w*.

B. Determine the unit rate of change for each table of values.

1.

	Independent Quantity	Dependent Quantity
Label	**Time**	**Height**
Units	**seconds**	**meters**
	0	0
	1	15
	2	30
	3	45
	4	60

2.

	Independent Quantity	Dependent Quantity
Label	**Time**	**Height**
Units	**seconds**	**meters**
	0	108
	1	96
	2	84
	3	72
	4	60

3.

	Independent Quantity	Dependent Quantity
Label	**Time**	**Depth**
Units	**minute**	**meters**
	0	0
	1	−14
	2	−28
	3	−42
	4	−56

4.

	Independent Quantity	Dependent Quantity
Label	**Time**	**Depth**
Units	**minute**	**feet**
	0	−520
	1	−455
	2	−390
	3	−325
	4	−260

Name ______________________________ Date ______________

5.

	Independent Quantity	Dependent Quantity
Label	**Time**	**Depth**
Units	**minutes**	**meters**
	0	0
	1	−18.5
	2	−37
	3	−55.5
	4	−74

6.

	Independent Quantity	Dependent Quantity
Label	**Time**	**Height**
Units	**seconds**	**feet**
	0	0
	1	13.2
	2	26.4
	3	39.6
	4	52.8

Topic 1

Introduction to Probability

Name ______________________________ Date ______________

I. Determining Probabilities

A. Write 0, $\frac{1}{2}$, or 1 to indicate the most appropriate probability for each event.

1. It will snow in Arizona in July.

2. Flipping a coin and landing on heads.

3. Rolling a standard six-sided number cube and landing on an integer.

4. The next baby born at your local hospital will be a boy.

5. The sun will shine in Long Beach, California, in July.

6. You will live to be over 120 years old.

B. You spin a spinner with equal-sized sections, as shown. Determine each probability.

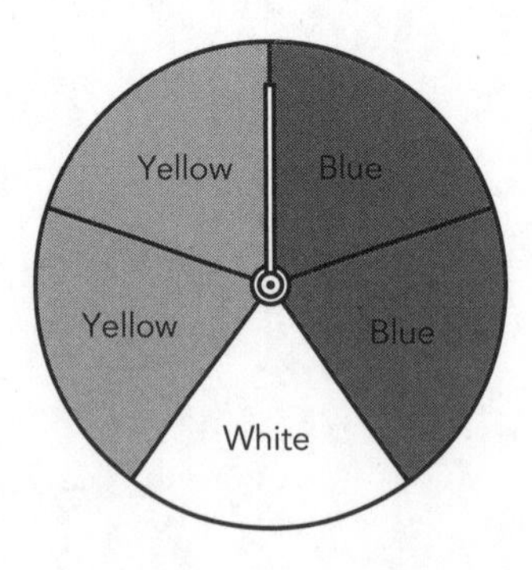

1. *P*(landing on White)

2. *P*(landing on Yellow)

Name ______________________________ Date ______________

3. P(landing on Blue)

4. P(not landing on Blue)

5. P(Yellow and Blue)

6. P(Yellow or Blue)

C. You choose a card from the deck of 46 cards shown. Determine each probability.

1. P(Diamond)

2. P(Rectangle)

3. *P*(Circle)

4. *P*(Star)

5. *P*(Star or Diamond)

6. *P*(not a Star)

7. *P*(Rectangle or Circle)

8. *P*(Circle and Star)

II. Probability Models

A. Construct a probability model for each situation. Determine whether the model is a uniform probability model or a non-uniform probability model.

1. Roll a 10-sided number polyhedron.

Outcome										
Probability										

Name ______________________________ Date ______________

2. Randomly select a painted rock from a bag containing 4 purple rocks, 3 green rocks, 3 orange rocks, and 2 blue rocks.

Outcome				
Probability				

3. Spin a spinner with 8 numbered sections of equal size.

Outcome								
Probability								

4. Randomly select 1 of 5 members of your hockey team to take the first shot in an overtime shootout.

Outcome					
Probability					

5. Spin a spinner with colored sections of equal size. The spinner has 3 blue sections, 3 red sections, and 2 yellow sections.

Outcome			
Probability			

6. Randomly select a female member of the Math Club whose members are Marcus, Isabella, Jasmine, Levi, Joseph, Belinda, Catherine, James, and Julia.

Outcome		
Probability		

7. Randomly select a day of the week to give your dog a bath by writing each day of the week on a slip of paper and choosing a slip of paper from a bag.

Outcome							
Probability							

8. Randomly choose a sock from a drawer that contains 4 black socks, 2 brown socks, and 2 blue socks.

Outcome			
Probability			

9. Toss a coin two times.

Outcome				
Probability				

Name ______________________________ Date ______________

10. Spin a spinner with equal sections. Four of the sections contain numbers and 8 of the sections contain letters.

Outcome		
Probability		

11. Randomly select a colored marble from a bag that contains 5 red marbles, 5 blue marbles, 5 green marbles, 5 yellow marbles, and 5 purple marbles.

Outcome					
Probability					

12. Randomly select a coin from a jar that contains 14 quarters, 26 dimes, 12 nickels, and 8 pennies.

Outcome				
Probability				

III. Determining Experimental Probabilities

A. Determine each experimental probability.

1. Suppose you toss a coin 20 times and record the results shown in the table. Complete the table and calculate the experimental probability of tossing tails.

Result	Tally	Total
Heads	卌 III	
Tails	卌 卌 II	

2. Suppose you roll a number cube 40 times and record the results shown in the table. Complete the table and calculate the experimental probability of rolling an even number.

Result	Tally	Total
1	卌	
2	卌 II	
3	IIII	
4	卌 I	
5	卌 卌	
6	卌 III	

Name ______________________________ Date ______________

3. Suppose you put two socks of one color and one sock of another color into a bag, and you choose one sock without looking. You repeat this 15 times, and you record the results shown in the table. Note that you always put the sock you chose back into the bag before choosing the next sock. Complete the table and calculate the experimental probability of choosing the sock that was a different color than the other two.

Result	Tally	Total
White	𝍸 𝍸 II	
Brown	III	

4. Suppose that you write the letters A, B, C, and D on four equal-size slips of paper. Then, you put them in a bag and choose one slip from the bag without looking. You repeat this 40 times and record the results shown in the table. Note that you always put the slip you chose back into the bag before choosing the next slip. Complete the table and calculate the experimental probability of choosing D.

Result	Tally	Total
A	𝍸 II	
B	𝍸 𝍸 II	
C	𝍸 𝍸 II	
D	𝍸 IIII	

5. Suppose that you put 2 dimes, 2 nickels, and 1 penny into a bag. Then, you choose one coin from the bag without looking, and record the results shown. You repeat this experiment 25 times. Note that you always put the coin you chose back into the bag before choosing the next coin. Complete the table and calculate the experimental probability of choosing a nickel.

Result	Tally	Total
Dime	卌 卌 II	
Nickel	卌 IIII	
Penny	IIII	

6. Suppose you use a paper clip as the arrow part of the spinner. You spin the spinner 30 times and record the data shown in the table. Complete the table and calculate the experimental probability of spinning a number greater than 1.

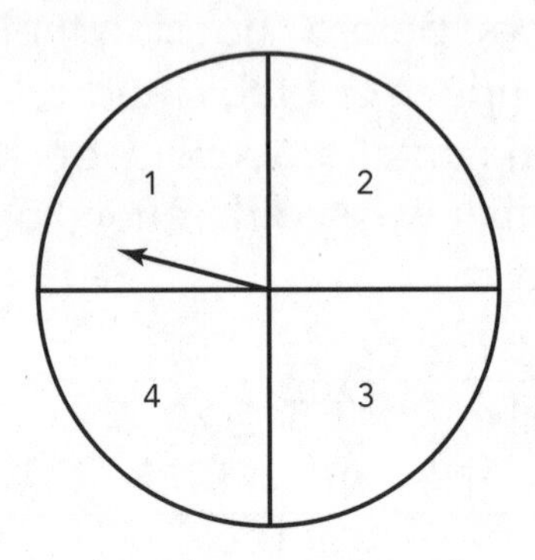

Result	Tally	Total
1	卌 I	
2	卌 IIII	
3	卌 II	
4	卌 III	

Topic 2

Compound Probability

Name ______________________________ Date ______________

I. Calculating Compound Probabilities

A. Determine each compound probability. Show your work.

A spinner has 6 equal parts labeled with the letters A through F.

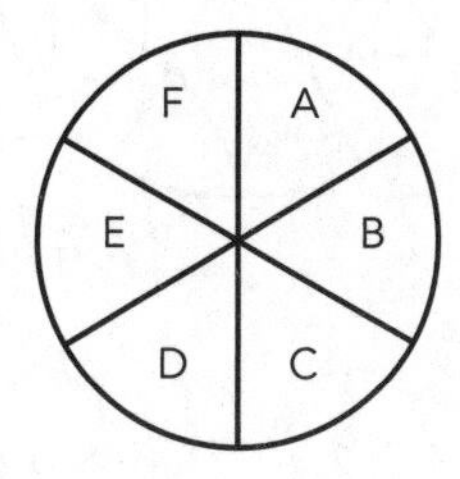

1. What is the probability that the next spin is an A or B?

2. What is the probability that the next spin is a vowel?

3. What is the probability that the next spin is not C?

4. What is the probability that the next spin is a consonant?

5. What is the probability that the next spin is a D, E, or F?

6. What is the probability that the next spin is not an A or B?

B. Determine each compound probability. Show your work.

A spinner has six equal parts labeled with the following shapes.

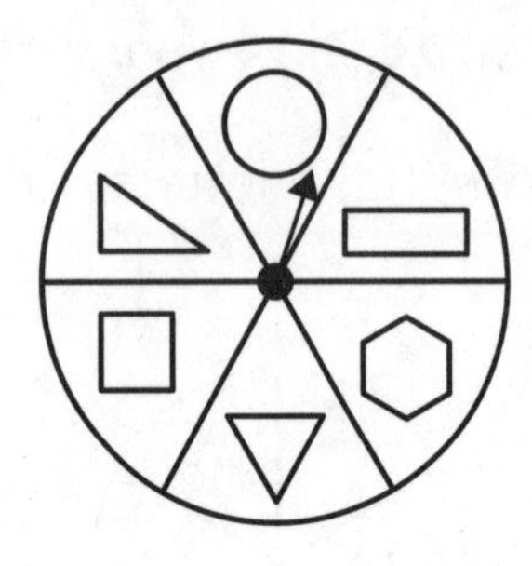

1. What is the probability that the next spin is a polygon?

2. What is the probability that the next spin is a parallelogram?

3. What is the probability that the next spin is a triangle or a circle?

4. What is the probability that the next spin is not a square?

5. What is the probability that the next spin is a shape with more than four sides?

6. What is the probability that the next spin is not an octagon?

Name ______________________ Date ____________

C. Determine each compound probability. Show your work.

A game requires spinning a spinner numbered 1 through 5 and rolling a six-sided number cube.

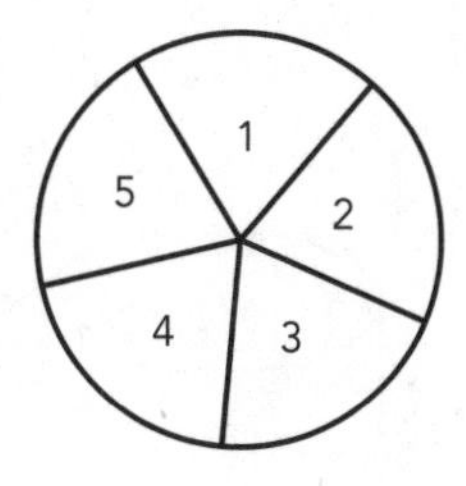

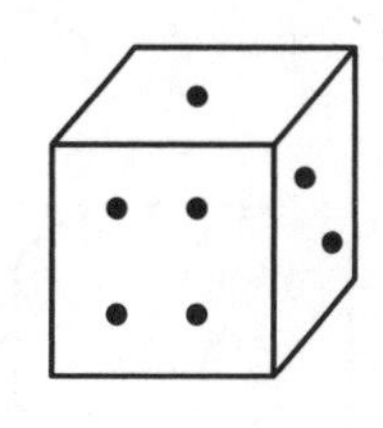

1. What is the probability of spinning an even number and rolling an even number?

2. What is the probability of spinning an odd number and rolling an odd number?

3. What is the probability of spinning a number less than 4 or rolling a number less than 4?

4. What is the probability of spinning a number greater than 3 or rolling a number greater than 3?

5. What is the probability of spinning a 5 or rolling a 5?

6. What is the probability of spinning a 6 or rolling a 6?

D. Determine each compound probability. Show your work.

Marbles were placed in two buckets. The first bucket contains 1 marble of each of the following colors: red, blue, green. The second bucket contains 1 marble of each of the following colors: yellow, green, purple, blue.

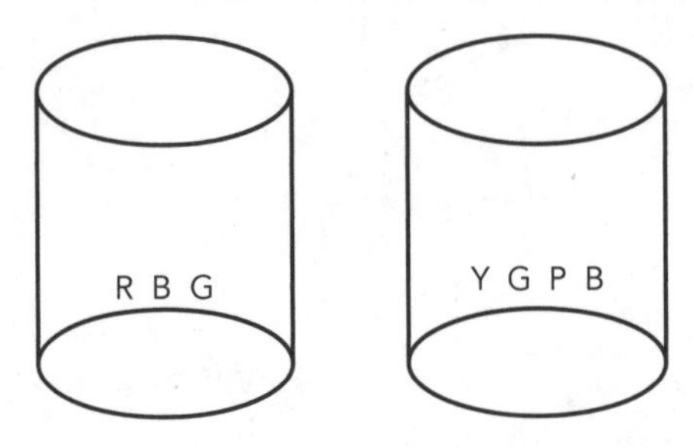

1. What is the probability of choosing two unique colors?

2. What is the probability of choosing green from the first bucket and green from the second bucket?

3. What is the probability of choosing blue from the first bucket or blue from the second bucket?

4. What is the probability of choosing yellow from the first bucket and purple from the second bucket?

5. What is the probability of choosing red from the first bucket or yellow from the second bucket?

6. What is the probability of choosing the same color from each bucket?

Topic 3

Drawing Inferences

Name ______________________________ Date ______________

I. Distinguishing Between Populations and Samples

A. Determine whether the data collected in each survey represent a census or a sample.

1. Ms. Carey concludes that 85% of the students in the school have at least one pet after she conducts a survey of the students in her class.

2. Paul reports that one out of every five boys on the boys' varsity basketball team can dunk a basketball after he conducts a survey of the boys on the team.

3. After examining eight cartons of eggs at a local supermarket, Sheila concludes that one out of every 12 eggs packaged in the U.S. is cracked.

4. Jorge surveys each of the teachers in his school. He concludes that 64% of the teachers in his school enjoy reading as a hobby.

5. After surveying each of the members of the Horse Club, Susana reports that four out of every five members own two or more horses.

6. Chris surveys each of the students in his seventh grade class. He concludes that 50% of all seventh graders have at least one sibling.

B. Determine whether each survey result is a parameter or a statistic.

1. According to an online poll, 35% of all U.S. citizens live in an apartment.

2. According to Ms. Carey's survey of the students in her class, 50% of her students have at least one dog.

3. A local newspaper conducted a survey last week. Of the 2300 subscribers, 1276 responded. Based on the survey, the editor concludes that 95% of the newspaper's subscribers will renew their subscription next year.

4. According to a random telephone survey of 1000 residents of Jackson County, 43% of the residents of Jackson County eat out at a restaurant more than once per week.

5. Mr. Rembrandt gives a survey to each of the students in the Art Club. He concludes that 90% of the Art Club members would like to visit the High Museum of Art in Atlanta.

6. The state police set up a roadblock on Highway 31 to determine how many drivers wear their seatbelts. They conclude that eight out of every ten drivers in Georgia wear their seatbelts.

Name ______________________ Date ____________

II. Identifying and Selecting Random Samples Using a Random Number Table

A. Determine if each given sample is random or not random. Explain your reasoning.

1. Rashid chooses each player on the soccer team whose last name starts with a vowel to participate in a survey about team sports.

2. Mr. Tamez chooses the first seven students to raise their hands in his math class to participate in a survey.

3. Ms. Patel, the chess team captain, writes the names of each of the twelve team members on separate slips of paper. She places the slips in a box, shakes it, and selects five slips with her eyes closed. The five members whose names are chosen will complete a survey about the chess team.

4. Ms. Searcy has 36 students in her English class. The students are seated in 6 rows. The students in each row are assigned a different number 1 through 6. Ms. Searcy rolls a 6-sided number cube to select a row. She rolls it again to select one of the students in that row. The selected student is given a survey about Ms. Searcy's English class.

5. A local restaurant is conducting a survey to determine the eating habits of the county's residents. They hand a survey to the first 50 customers of the day.

6. Customers at Bull's Eye Grocery can win a $25 gift card for throwing a bull's eye on the dart board after they check out. Winners are also given a survey about their shopping experience at Bull's Eye Grocery.

B. Use Ms. Saunders' Class List and the Random Number Table at the end of this Skills Practice to answer each question.

Ms. Saunders' Class List			
Student Name	Student Number	Student Name	Student Number
Amos (M)	11	Jerome (M)	21
Emilio (M)	12	Cristina (F)	22
Julia (F)	13	Pedro (M)	23
Olivia (F)	14	Jada (F)	24
Mattie (F)	15	Wei (F)	25
Aki (M)	16	Lakyta (F)	26
Sherwin (M)	17	Nelson (M)	27
Noah (M)	18	Tonya (F)	28
Belinda (F)	19	Luisa (F)	29
Mario (M)	20	Lavon (M)	30

1. The students in Ms. Saunders' class are each given a student number (11 through 30) as shown in the class list. Use line 14 of the Random Number Table to determine the first four random student numbers.

2. Ms. Saunders randomly selects 3 students in her class according to their student number. She uses line 18 of the Random Number Table. What are the students' names?

3. Ms. Saunders randomly selects 3 boys in her class using line 8 of the Random Number Table. What are the students' names?

4. Ms. Saunders randomly selects 3 girls in her class using line 10 of the Random Number Table. What are the students' names?

5. Ms. Saunders randomly selects 2 girls in her class using line 20 of the Random Number Table. What are the students' names?

6. Ms. Saunders randomly selects 2 boys in her class using line 15 of the Random Number Table. What are the students' names?

Name ____________________ Date ____________

III. Comparing the Measures of Center and Variation for Two Populations

A. Compare the means and the mean absolute deviations of the data sets in each problem.

1. Set 1: 4, 10, 2, 8, 10 Set 2: 4, 10, 40, 8, 10

2. Set 1: 35, 18, 58, 65, 29 Set 2: 19, 26, 45, 73, 27

3. Set 1: 61, 55, 57, 64, 86 Set 2: 62, 49, 9, 92, 15

4. Set 1: 24, 21, 24, 30, 26 Set 2: 59, 33, 83, 94, 11

5. The Cupcake Cupboard recently added two new flavors of cupcake to their selection—mocha and cinnamon. The store randomly selected 20 customers and asked them to rate the flavors on a scale of 0 to 100. The results of the survey are shown in the dot plot.

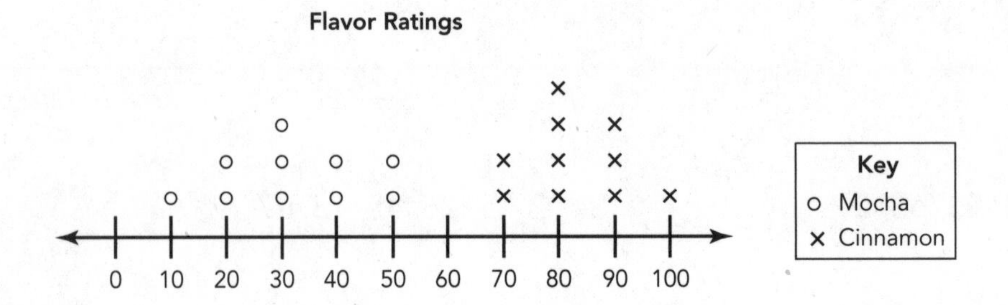

6. Mr. Reidel randomly selected ten students each from his first and fourth period math classes and used their quiz scores to create the dot plot shown.

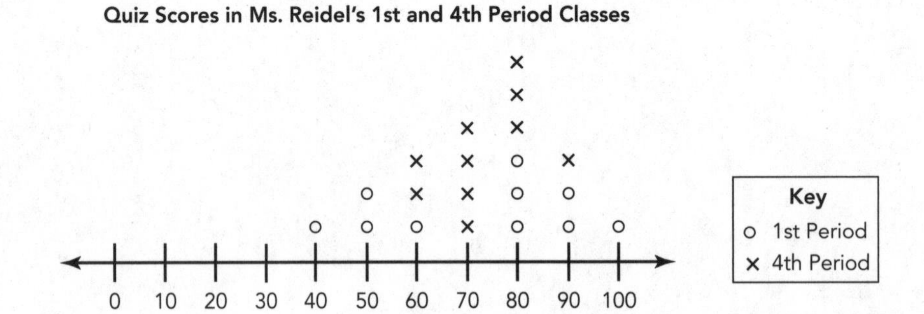

Name ______________________________ Date ______________

IV. Comparing Distributions

A. Compare the medians and the IQRs of the data sets in each problem.

1. Set 1: 16, 97, 59, 54, 28 Set 2: 29, 47, 85, 96, 52

2. Set 1: 29, 62, 16, 65, 83, 62, 96, 61 Set 2: 78, 13, 79, 87, 68, 4, 68, 98

3. Set 1: 96, 59, 50, 47, 42, 97, 29 Set 2: 12, 63, 97, 52, 91, 71, 2

4. Consider the data sets represented by the box-and-whisker plots.

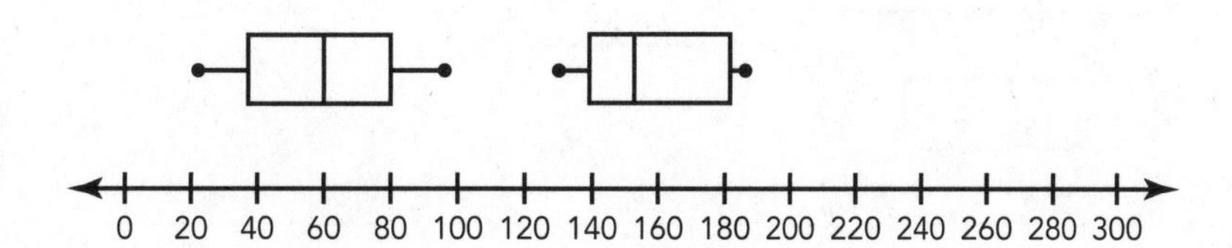

5. Consider the data sets represented by the box-and-whisker plots.

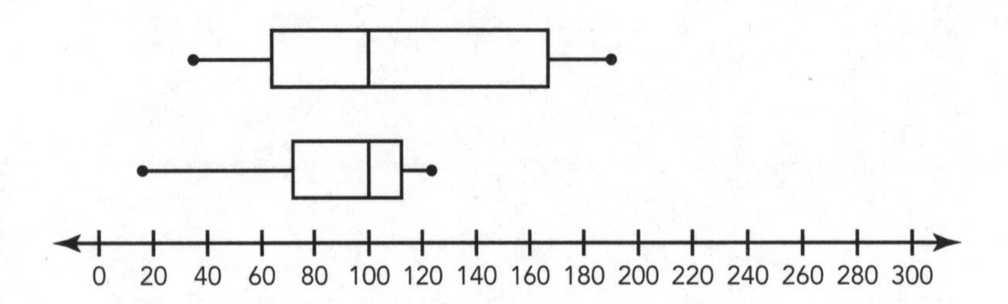

6. Consider the data sets represented by the box-and-whisker plots.

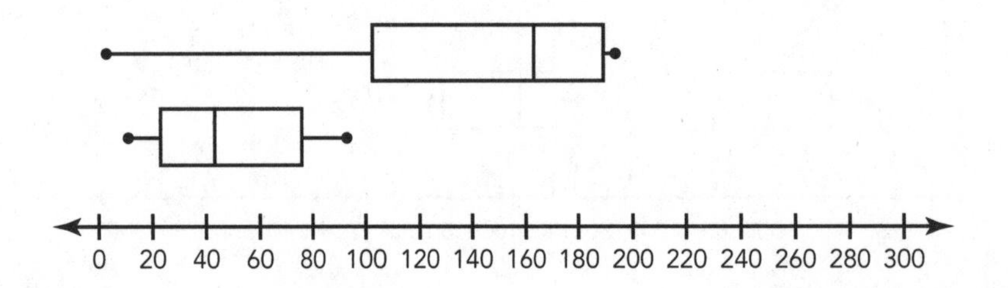

Name ______________________________ Date ______________

Random Number Table										
Line 1	65285	97198	12138	53010	94601	15838	16805	61404	43516	17020
Line 2	17264	57327	38224	29301	18164	38109	34976	65692	98566	29550
Line 3	95639	99754	31199	92558	68368	04985	51092	37780	40261	14479
Line 4	61555	76404	86214	11808	12840	55147	97438	60222	12645	62090
Line 5	78137	98768	04689	87130	79225	08153	84967	64539	79493	74917
Line 6	62490	99215	84987	28759	19107	14733	24550	28067	68894	38490
Line 7	24216	63444	21283	07044	92729	37284	13211	37485	11415	36457
Line 8	18975	95428	33226	55901	31605	43816	22259	00317	46999	98571
Line 9	59138	39542	71168	57609	91510	27904	74244	50940	31553	62562
Line 10	29478	59652	50414	31966	87912	87154	12944	49862	96566	48825
Line 11	96155	95009	27429	72918	08457	78134	48407	26061	58754	05326
Line 12	29621	66583	62966	12468	20245	14015	04014	35713	03980	03024
Line 13	12639	75291	71020	17265	41598	64074	64629	63293	53307	48766
Line 14	14544	37134	54714	02401	63228	26831	19386	15457	17999	18306
Line 15	83403	88827	09834	11333	68431	31706	26652	04711	34593	22561
Line 16	67642	05204	30697	44806	96989	68403	85621	45556	35434	09532
Line 17	64041	99011	14610	40273	09482	62864	01573	82274	81446	32477
Line 18	17048	94523	97444	59904	16936	39384	97551	09620	63932	03091
Line 19	93039	89416	52795	10631	09728	68202	20963	02477	55494	39563
Line 20	82244	34392	96607	17220	51984	10753	76272	50985	97593	34320

Topic 1

Angles and Triangles

Name ______________________________ Date ________________

I. Classifying Angles

A. Identify each pair of angles as complementary angles, supplementary angles, or vertical angles.

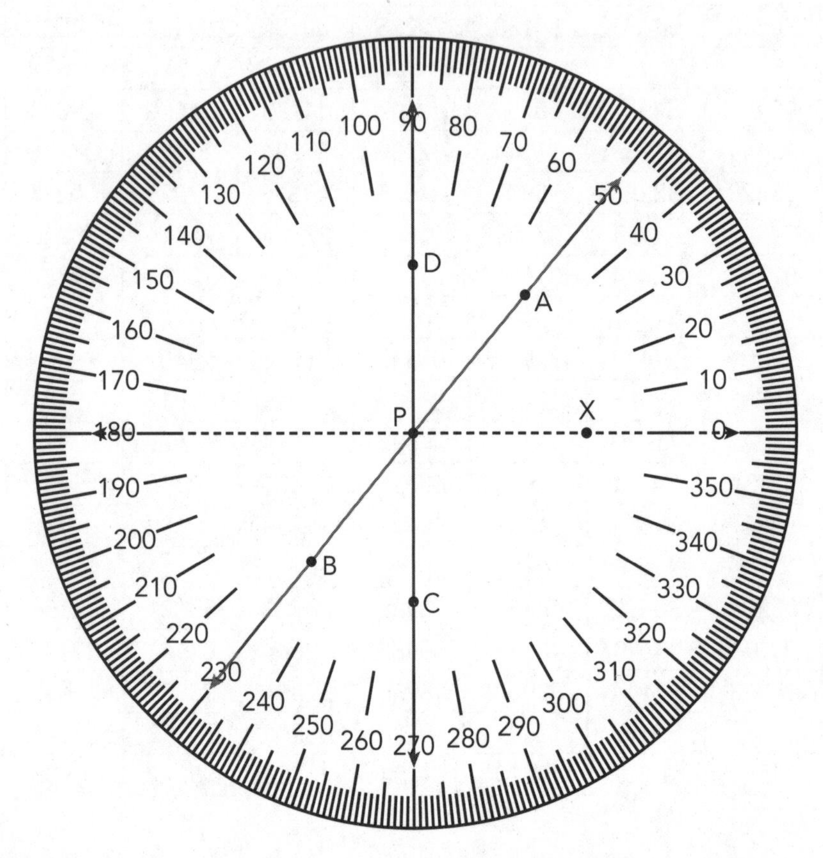

1. angles *DPA* and *APC*

2. angles *DPA* and *CPB*

3. angles *DPA* and *BPD*

4. angles *APC* and *CPB*

5. angles *APC* and *BPD*

6. angles *APX* and *APD*

Name ____________________ Date ____________

B. Use the figure to identify each pair of angles as complementary angles, supplementary angles, vertical angles, or none of these.

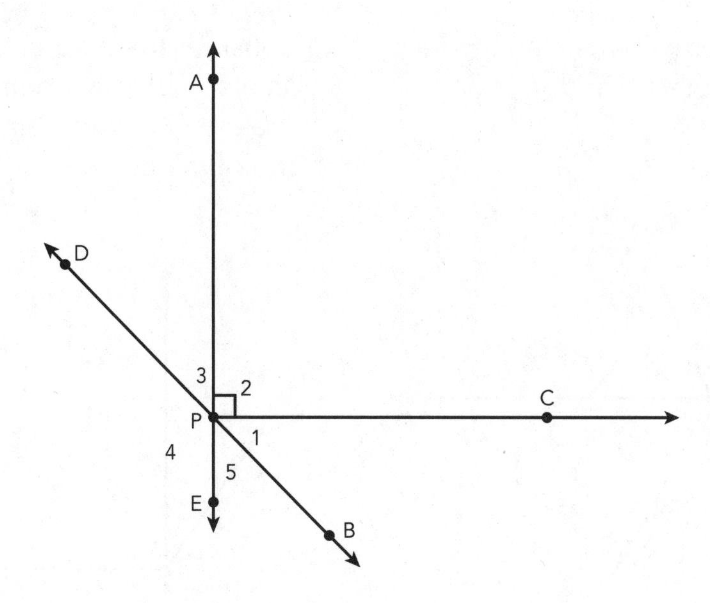

1. angles 2 and 4

2. angles 1 and 5

3. angles 3 and 5

4. angles 3 and 4

5. angles 3 and 1

6. angles 4 and 5

II. Solving for Unknown Angles

A. Determine each unknown measure.

1. Consider the diagram. Points T and R lie on a straight line. Points S and V lie on a straight line.

S
T
115°
P
x°
x°
R
V
Q

Determine the value of x.

2. Consider the diagram. Points A and E lie on a straight line, points P and C lie on a straight line, and points B and D lie on a straight line.

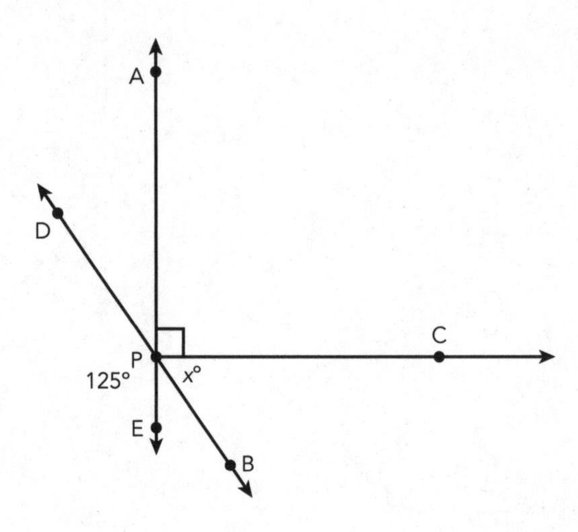

Determine the value of x.

Name ______________________________ Date ______________

3. Consider the diagram. Points B and C lie on a straight line.

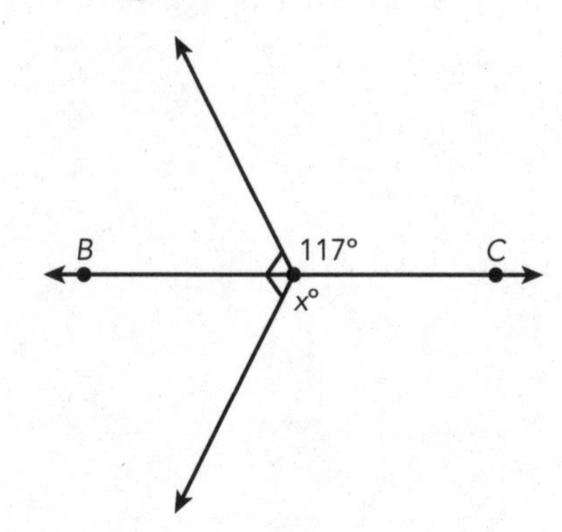

Determine the value of x.

4. Consider the diagram. Points A and B lie on a straight line and points D and F lie on a straight line.

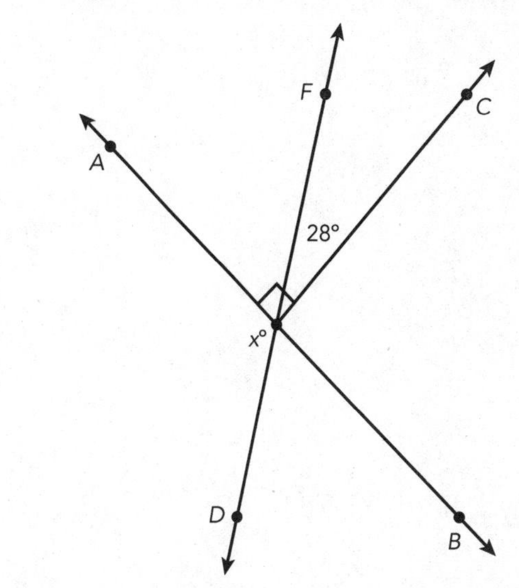

Determine the value of x.

5. Consider the diagram. Points J and N lie on a straight line, points K and P lie on a straight line, and points M and R lie on a straight line.

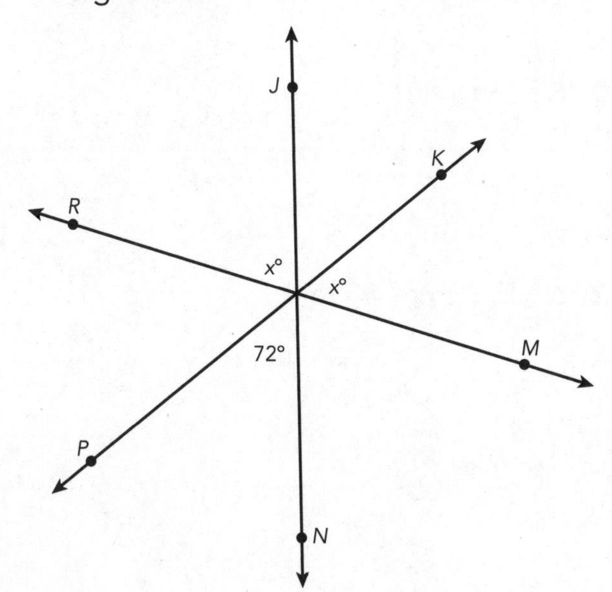

Determine the value of x.

6. Consider the diagram. Points W and Y lie on a straight line and points X and Z lie on a straight line.

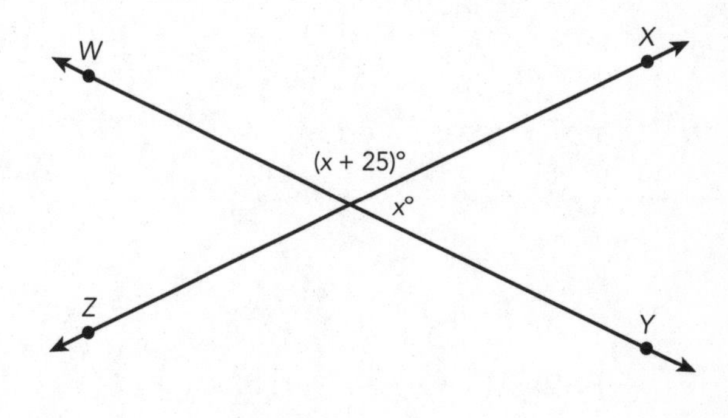

Determine the value of x.

III. Triangle Inequality Theorem

A. Determine whether it is possible to form a triangle using segments with the given measurements.

1. 3 in., 2.9 in., 5 in.

2. 8 ft, 9 ft, 11 ft

3. 4 m, 5.1 m, 12.5 m

4. 7.4 cm, 8.1 cm, 9.8 cm

5. 10 yd, 5 yd, 21 yd

6. 13.8 km, 6.3 km, 7.5 km

7. 112 mm, 300 mm, 190 mm

8. 20.2 in., 11 in., 8.2 in.

9. 30 cm, 12 cm, 17 cm

10. 8 ft, 8 ft, 8 ft

11. 10 m, 8 m, 1 m

12. 6 cm, 3.1 cm, 9 cm

Topic 2

Three-Dimensional Figures

Name ______________________________ Date ______________

I. Calculating Volume of Pyramids

A. Determine each volume. Show your work.

1. The given figure is a square pyramid. The side length of the base of the pyramid is 5 inches. The height of the pyramid is 3.3 inches. What is the volume of the pyramid?

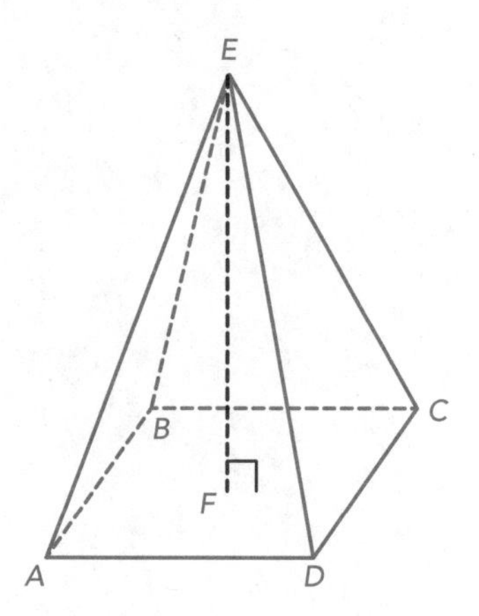

2. You buy a spinning top for your younger cousin. The spinning top is a square pyramid. The side length of the base of the spinning top is 32 millimeters. The height of the spinning top is 32 millimeters. What is the volume of the spinning top?

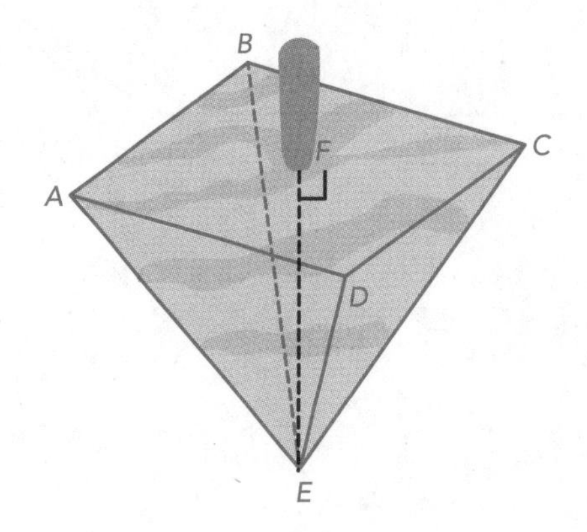

3. The given figure is a square pyramid. The side length of the base of the pyramid is 6.6 feet. The height of the pyramid is 12.672 feet. What is the volume of the pyramid?

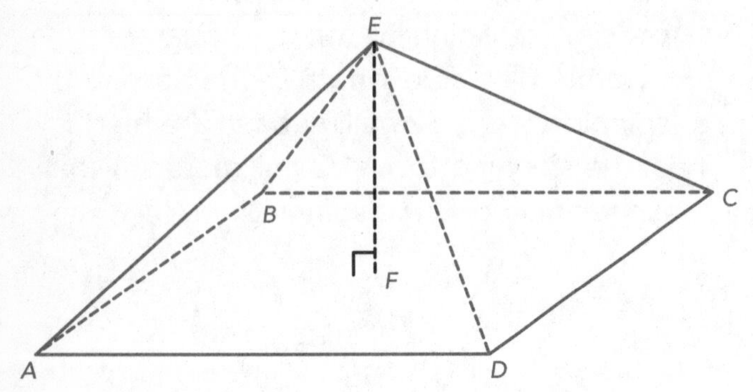

4. Your aunt is building a new fence around her front yard. The top of each fence post is a square pyramid. The side length of the base of the fence post top is 10.1 centimeters. The height of the fence post top is 6.868 centimeters. What is the volume of the fence post top?

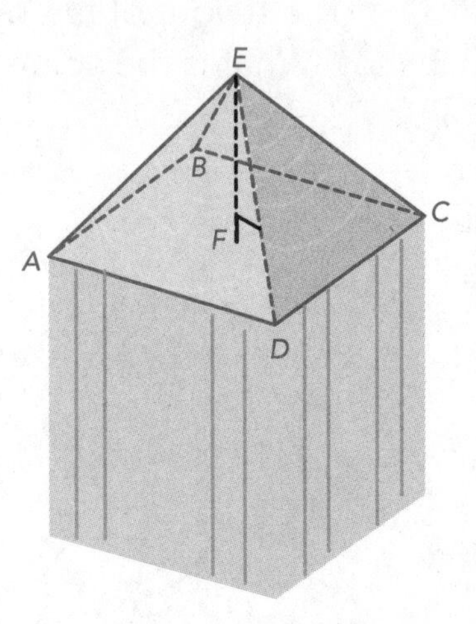

Name ______________________________ Date ______________

5. The given figure is a square pyramid. The side length of the base of the pyramid is 28 millimeters. The height of the pyramid is 14 millimeters. What is the volume of the pyramid?

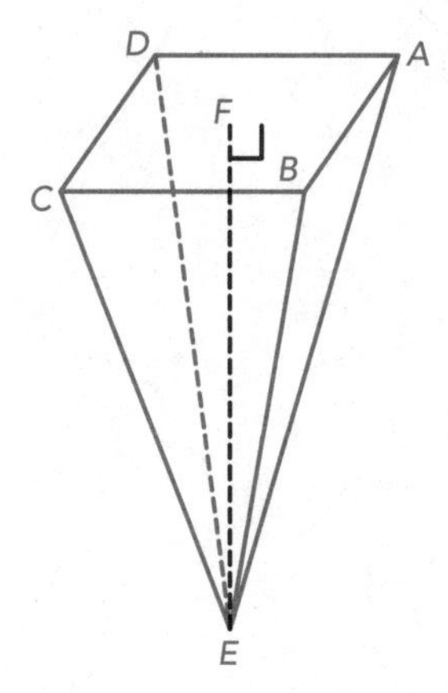

6. You see a salt shaker at a local restaurant. The top of the salt shaker is a square pyramid. The side length of the base of the salt shaker top is 15 millimeters. The height of the salt shaker top is 7.5 millimeters. What is the volume of the salt shaker top?

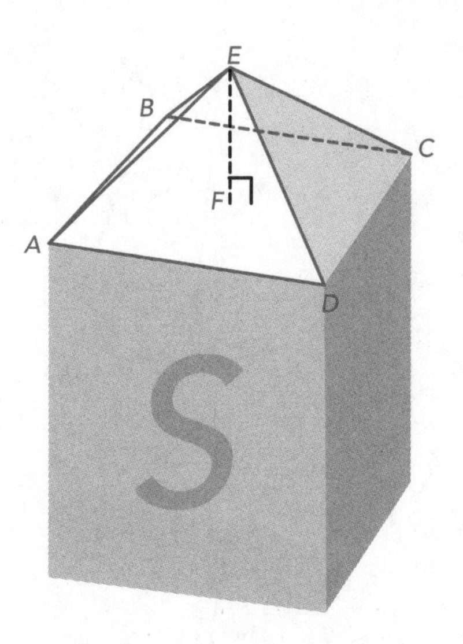

II. Calculating Surface Area of Pyramids

A. Calculate the surface area of each pyramid.

1.

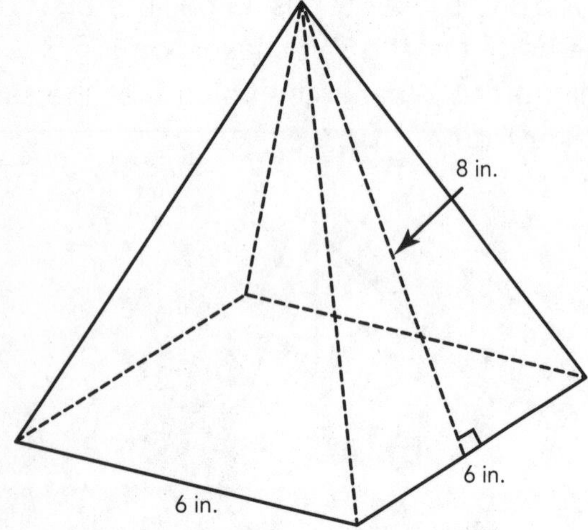

2.

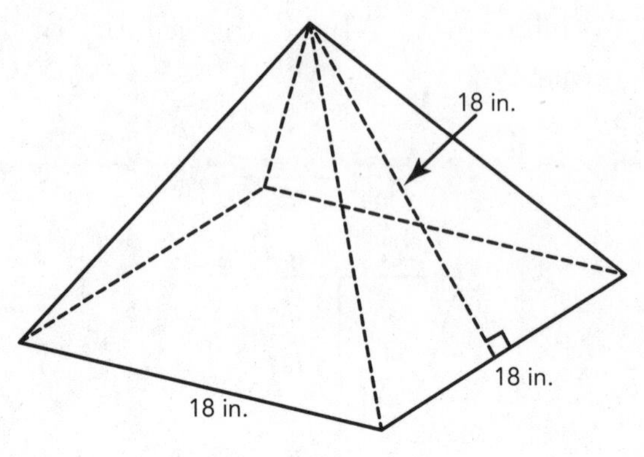

3.

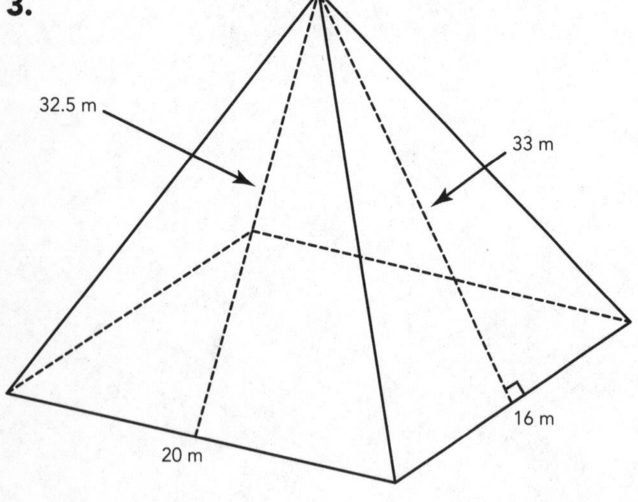

4.

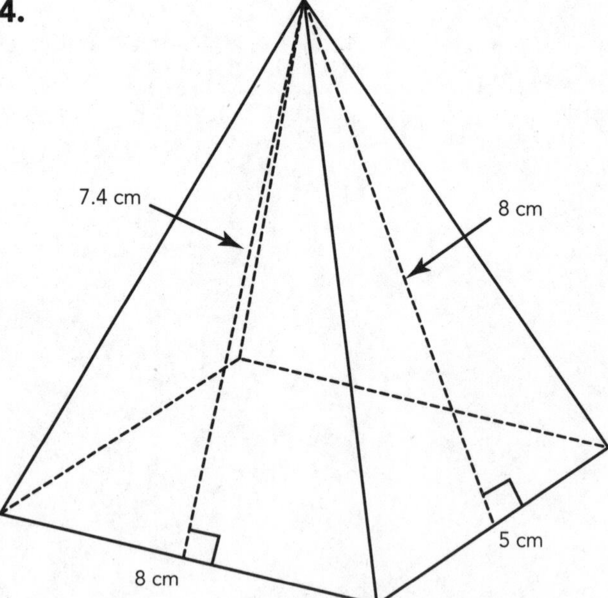

Name ____________________ Date ____________________

5.

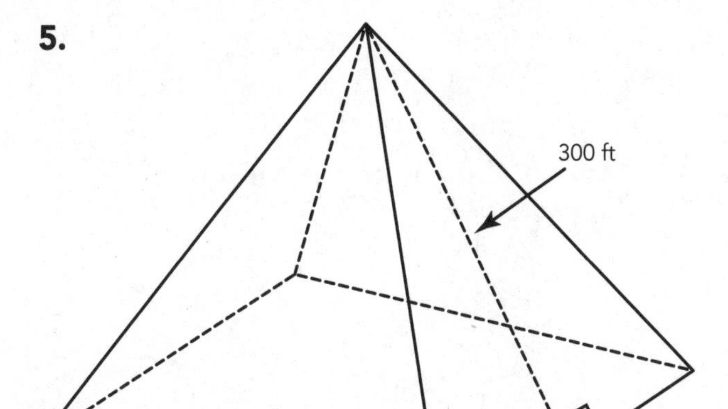

6.

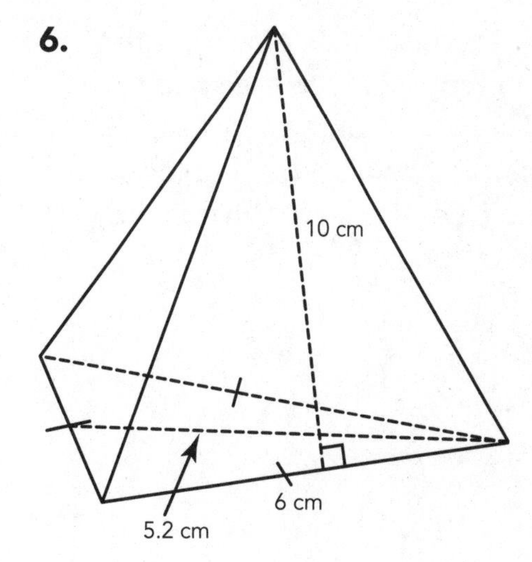

III. Using Volume of Pyramids

A. Answer each question.

1. Your uncle is having a new roof installed on his house. The roof is a square pyramid. The side length of the base of the roof is 28 feet. The volume of the roof is 1829.3333 cubic feet. What is the height of the roof?

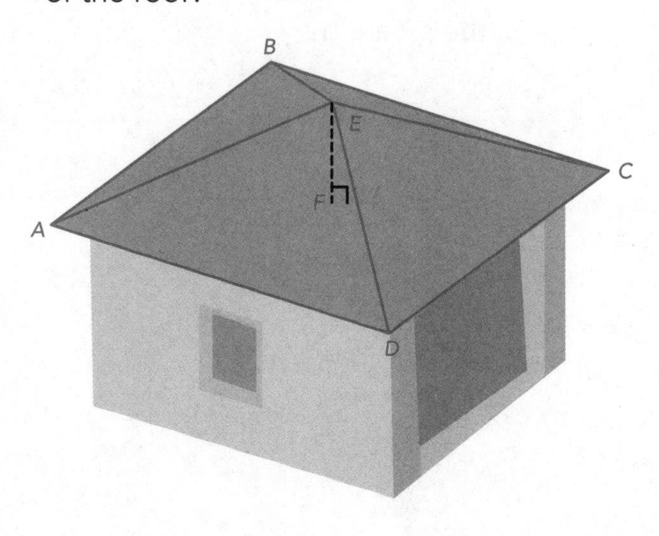

2. A local business is planning to open a new office located at the top of a skyscraper. The office space is a square pyramid. The side length of the base of the office space is 34 feet. The volume of the office space is 13,101.333 cubic feet. What is the height of the office space?

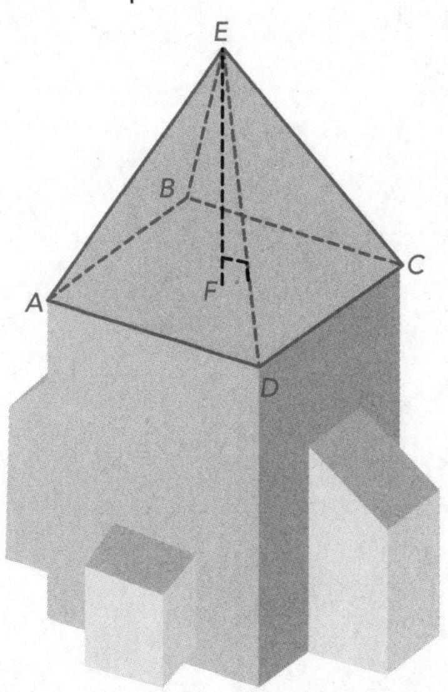

3. Your younger cousin likes playing with blocks. One type of block is a square pyramid. The height of the block is 8.844 centimeters. The volume of the block is 57.0733 cubic centimeters. What is the side length of the base of the block?

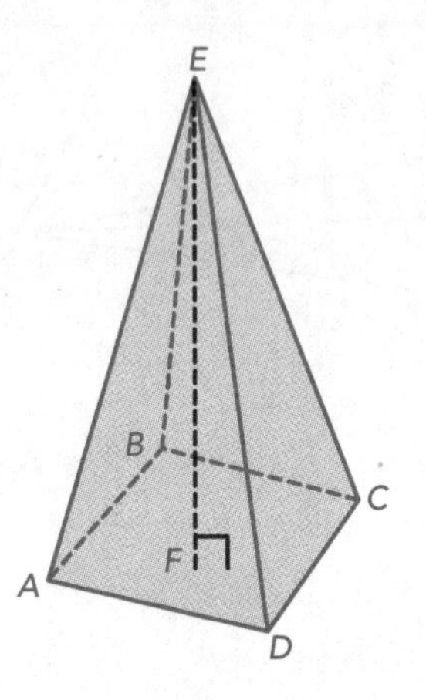

4. The given figure is a square pyramid. The height of the pyramid is 22 inches. The volume of the pyramid is 3549.3333 cubic inches. What is the side length of the base of the pyramid?

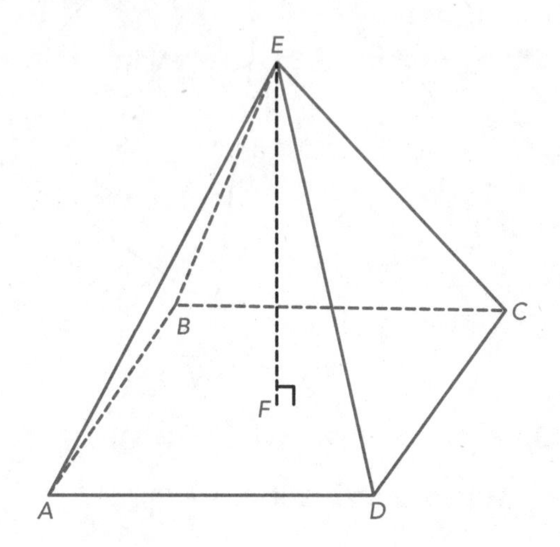

5. Your aunt buys a set of drinking glasses. Each glass is a square pyramid. The side length of the base of the glass is 6.9 centimeters. The volume of the glass is 222.2911 cubic centimeters. What is the height of the glass?

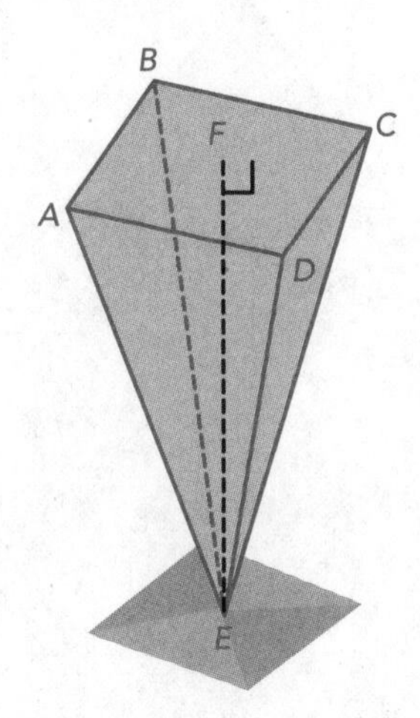

6. The given figure is a square pyramid. The height of the pyramid is 5 millimeters. The volume of the pyramid is 166.6667 cubic millimeters. What is the side length of the base of the pyramid?

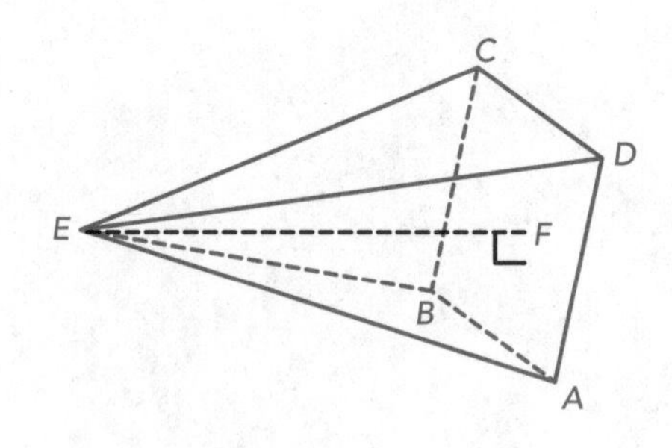

MODULE 1

Topic 1

Circles and Ratio

I. A.

1a. Circle B
1b. Sample answer: line segment AB
1c. Sample answer: line segment AD
1d. Sample answer: line segment CF

3a. Circle C
3b. Sample answer: line segment CE
3c. Sample answer: line segment AD
3d. Sample answer: line segment FB

5a. Circle E
5b. Sample answer: line segment EF
5c. Sample answer: line segment AB
5d. Sample answer: line segment DC

I. B.

1. The diameter of Circle A equals the diameter of Circle D, so the circles are congruent.

3. The radius of Circle A equals the radius of Circle B, so the circles are congruent.

5. The diameter of Circle A equals the diameter of Circle B, so the circles are congruent.

II. A.

1. 18.84 cm

3. 23.55 in.

5. 43.96 cm

II. B.

1. $d = 17.83$ cm

3. $d = 35.92$ mm

5. $d = 15.2$ mm

II. C.

1. 7.07 cm^2

3. 113.04 $in.^2$

5. 200.96 $in.^2$

III. A.

1. $r = 7$ in., $d = 14$ in., $A = 153.86$ in.^{2}
3. $r = 6$ in., $d = 12$ in., $A = 113.04$ in.^{2}
5. $r = 11$ in., $C = 69.08$ in., $A = 379.94$ in.^{2}

III. B.

1. The pool will cover about 114.93 square feet.
3. Carlos needs 12.56 feet of rubber edging.
5. Eva needs at least 15.64 feet of the paper streamer.

Topic 2

Fractional Rates

I. A.

1. $\dfrac{\frac{1}{50}\text{ cent}}{1\text{ kilobyte}}$
3. $\dfrac{\frac{1}{2}\text{ cent}}{1\text{ toss}}$
5. $\dfrac{\frac{22}{25}\text{ cent}}{1\text{ pack}}$
7. $\dfrac{\frac{1}{5}\text{ cent}}{1\text{ cup}}$

I. B.

1. $\frac{1}{6}$ cup per batch or 6 batches per cup
3. $2\frac{2}{3}$ pound per tablespoon or $\frac{3}{8}$ tablespoon per pound
5. 30 pages an hour or $\frac{1}{30}$ hour per page

II. A.

1. Marcus: 80 words per minute; Rhys: $66\frac{2}{3}$ words per minute; Marcus types faster.
3. Maggie's computer: $8\frac{2}{5}$ megabytes per minute; Brooke's computer: $7\frac{1}{5}$ megabytes per minute; Maggie's computer downloads faster.
5. Beth: $\frac{1}{12}$ gallon per mile; Martha: $\frac{1}{15}$ gallon per mile; Martha used fewer gallons of gas per mile.

III. A.

1. 9 centimeters
3. 245 pounds
5. 604 pounds
7. $104
9. 27 boys
11. $19

IV. A.

1. 80 games
3. 504 people
5. 348 times
7. 90 pounds
9. 3 gallons
11. 400 calories

Topic 3

Proportionality

I. A.

1a. 34 gallons
1b. 14 minutes
1c. $\frac{2}{17}$
1d. $\frac{17}{2}$

3a. 36 cases of shoes
3b. 72 boxes of socks
3c. $\frac{8}{3}$
3d. $\frac{3}{8}$

5a. 16 pennies
5b. 30 grams
5c. $\frac{2}{5}$
5d. $\frac{5}{2}$

II. A.

1.

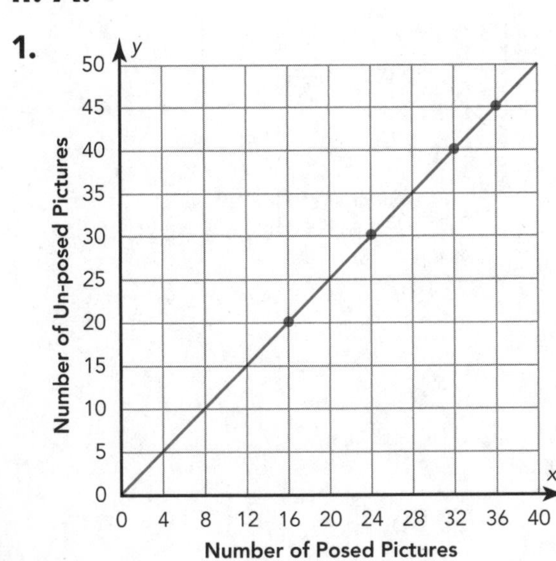

$\frac{u}{p} = \frac{5}{4}$

3.

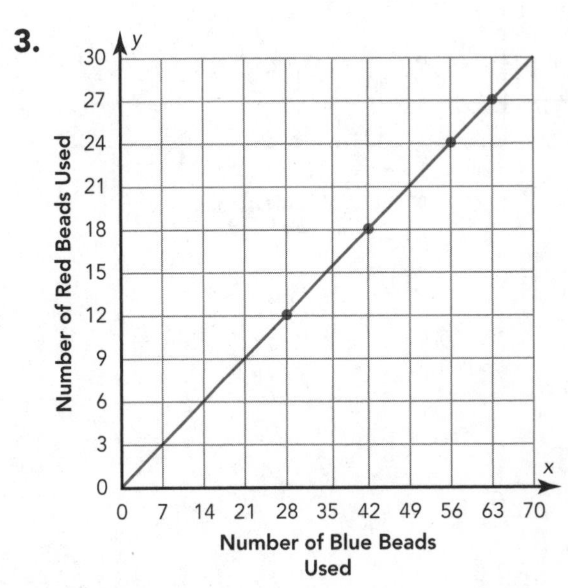

$\frac{r}{b} = \frac{3}{7}$

5.

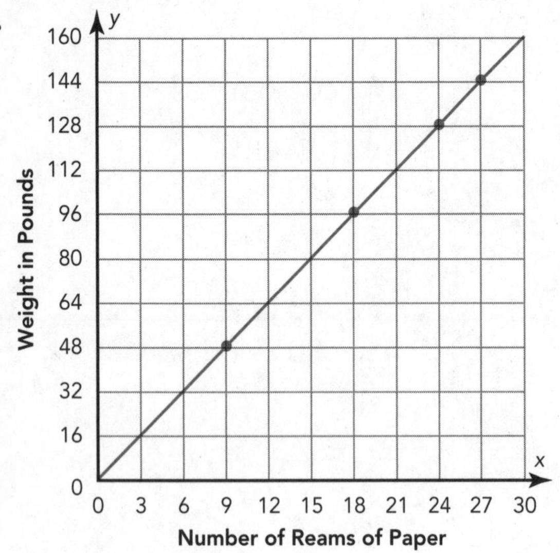

$\frac{p}{r} = \frac{16}{3}$

7.

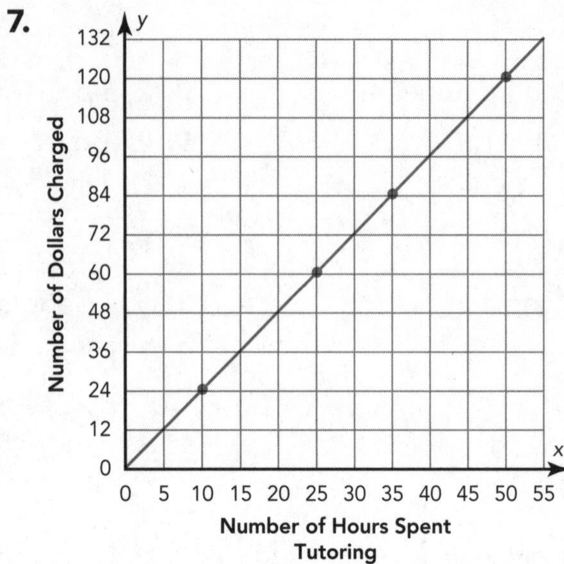

$\frac{d}{h} = \frac{12}{5}$

9.

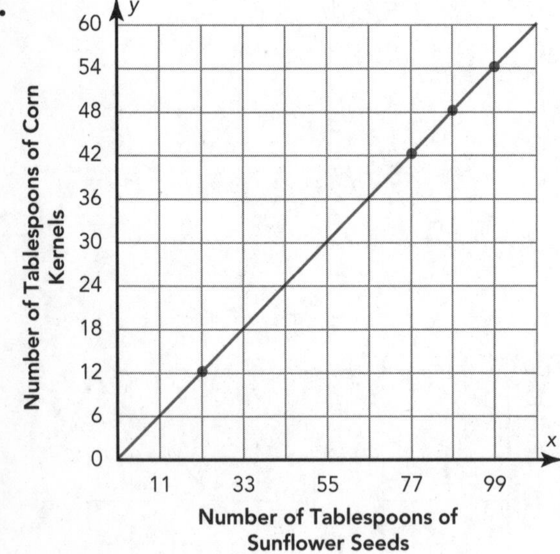

$\frac{k}{s} = \frac{6}{11}$

11.

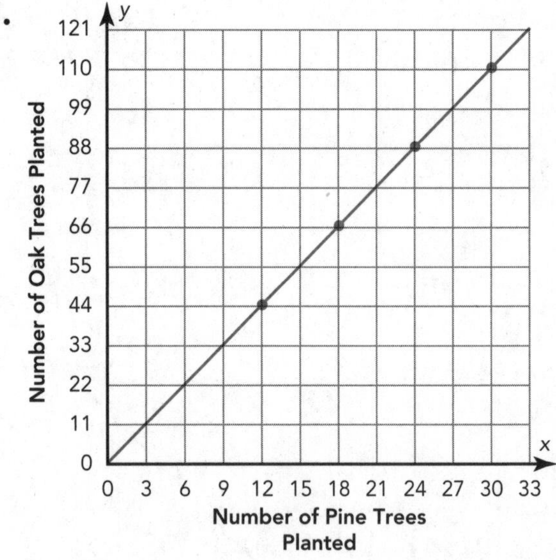

$\frac{k}{p} = \frac{11}{3}$

II. B.

1a. $\frac{20}{3}$

1b. $\frac{r}{s} = \frac{20}{3}$

1c. $r = \frac{20}{3}s$

3a. $\frac{17}{5}$

3b. $\frac{c}{m} = \frac{17}{5}$

3c. $c = \frac{17}{5}m$

5a. $\frac{10}{3}$

5b. $\frac{m}{h} = \frac{10}{3}$

5c. $m = \frac{10}{3}h$

7a. $\frac{3}{2}$

7b. $\frac{c}{v} = \frac{3}{2}$

7c. $c = \frac{3}{2}v$

9a. $\frac{5}{6}$

9b. $\frac{r}{b} = \frac{5}{6}$

9c. $r = \frac{5}{6}b$

11a. $\frac{9}{5}$

11b. $\frac{f}{n} = \frac{9}{5}$

11c. $f = \frac{9}{5}n$

II. C.

1. Yes

3. No

5. No

7. No

9. No

11. No

II. D.

1.

Number of Insects	Number of Butterflies
insects	butterflies
15	4
45	12
180	48
540	144

y
200
180
160
140
120
100
80
60
40
20
0
Number of Butterflies
x
0 60 120 180 240 300 360 420 480 540 600
Number of Insects

3.

Total Baskets	Jump-shots
baskets	jump-shots
10	6
25	15
55	33
130	78

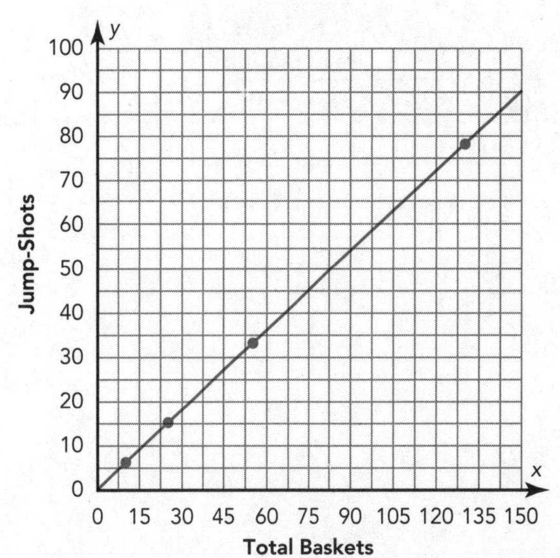

5.

Total Drawings	Still Lifes
drawings	still lifes
15	6
30	12
65	26
140	56

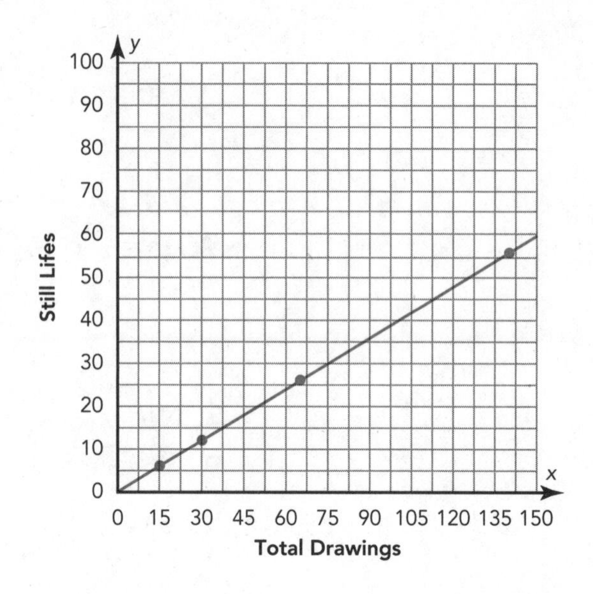

7.

Total Yards Lost	Yards Lost Due to Slippery Conditions
yards	yards
12	4
15	5
45	15
72	24

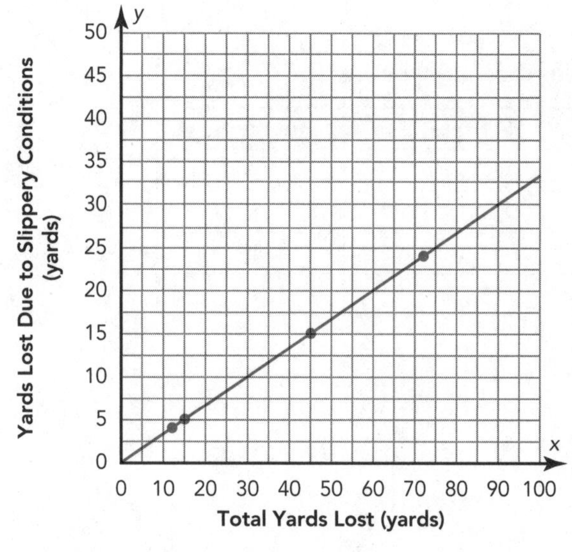

9.

Total Students	Students Who Danced
students	students
105	30
140	40
315	90
385	110

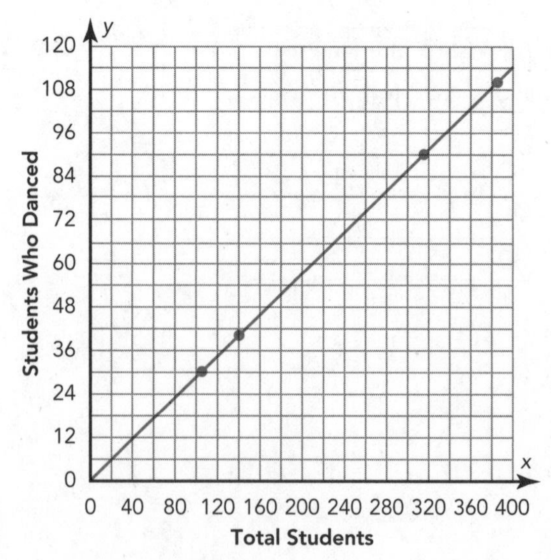

11.

Number of Pages in Report	Number of Pages Mangled
pages	pages
5	1
10	2
40	8
65	13

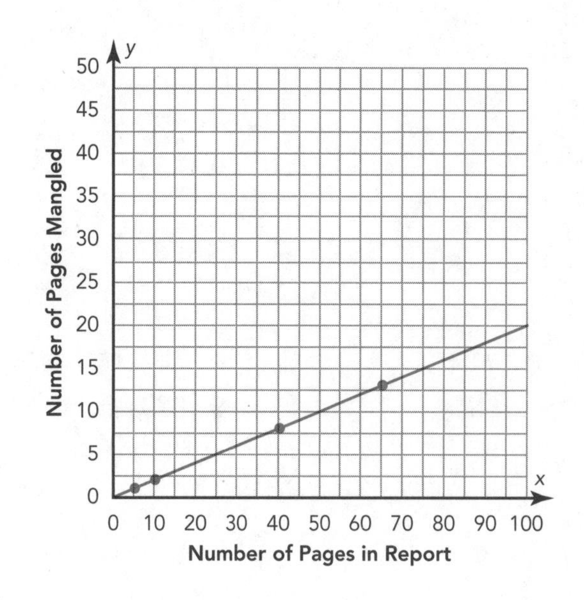

Topic 4

Proportional Relationships

I. A.

1. 0.6%

3. 7.5%

5. 0.3%

I. B.

1. $\frac{2}{100}$, 0.02, 2%

3. 0.8%, 0.008, $\frac{4}{500}$

5. $6\frac{7}{10}$%, 0.067, $\frac{67}{1000}$

7. $\frac{12}{1000}$, 0.012, 1.2%

9. 0.5%, 0.005, $\frac{1}{200}$

11. 0.006, 0.6%, $\frac{6}{1000}$

I. C.

1. 1%

3. $30

5. 84.6 minutes

I. D.

1. 39

3. 22%

5. 200

PAGE 140

I. E.

1. 80%
3. about 17%
5. $29.62
7. $40
9. $33

II. A.

1. 75% decrease
3. 75% increase
5. 55% increase
7. 65% decrease
9. 88% increase
11. 25% decrease

II. B.

1. 18 customers
3. 54 seats
5. 8 beats per minute
7. $35
9. 53 pizzas
11. 27 sports cards

III. A.

1. 2,680 ft
3. 180 yd
5. 60 ft

MODULE 2

Topic 1

Adding and Subtracting Rational Numbers

I. A.

1. −12
3. 0
5. 6
7. −11
9. −7
11. −14

PAGE 141

II. A.

1. -5
3. -11
5. -2
7. -6
9. -17
11. 10

II. B.

1. 7
3. 9
5. -5
7. 20
9. -14
11. 7

II. C.

1. $+$
3. $+$
5. $-$

II. D.

1. -3
3. 8
5. -4
7. 22
9. -13
11. -7

III. A.

1. -21°C
3. -50.1 feet
5. $-52\frac{5}{12}$ feet

Topic 2

Multiplying and Dividing Rational Numbers

I. A.

1. $-8 \times (-7) = 56$
   $-7 \times (-8) = 56$
   $56 \div (-8) = -7$
   $56 \div (-7) = -8$
3. $-7 \times 5 = -35$
   $5 \times (-7) = -35$
   $-35 \div 5 = -7$
   $-35 \div (-7) = 5$
5. $-7 \times 3 = -21$
   $3 \times (-7) = -21$
   $-21 \div (-7) = 3$
   $-21 \div 3 = -7$
7. $-12 \times (-4) = 48$
   $-4 \times (-12) = 48$
   $48 \div (-12) = -4$
   $48 \div (-4) = -12$
9. $-3 \times 3 = -9$
   $3 \times (-3) = -9$
   $-9 \div (-3) = 3$
   $-9 \div 3 = -3$
11. $10 \times (-2) = -20$
    $-2 \times 10 = -20$
    $-20 \div 10 = -2$
    $-20 \div -2 = 10$

II. A.

1. −18 **3.** −121 **5.** 30

7. −55 **9.** −64 **11.** −60

II. B.

1. −10 **3.** −1 **5.** 11

7. −8 **9.** −7 **11.** −20

II. C.

1. −4 **3.** 70 **5.** −5

7. −33 **9.** −7 **11.** −72

III. A.

1. 8 **3.** −32 **5.** 47

7. 24 **9.** 11 **11.** $-\frac{1}{6}$

III. B.

1. 5.2 **3.** 6.54 **5.** $-7\frac{2}{5}$

7. $\frac{8}{9}$ **9.** 99.87 **11.** 15

MODULE 3

Topic 1

Algebraic Expressions

I. A.

1. h = hours you skate
$3 + 2h$
a. \$7
b. \$11
c. \$10

3. s = number of snacks bought
$20 - 1.25s$
a. \$17.50
b. \$11.25
c. \$5

5. a = number of additional lessons
$\frac{a+7}{12}$
a. 1
b. 3
c. 5

7. m = number of miles traveled
$2.5m + 4.50$
a. \$17
b. \$44.50
c. \$35.75

9. c = number of cards
$\frac{c}{18}$
a. 5 pages
b. 8 pages
c. 10 pages

11. t = number of tickets
$1.5t + 8$
a. \$20
b. \$45.50
c. \$68

II. A.

1. $3(3x + 1) = 9x + 3$

3. $4(-2x - 3) = -8x - 12$

5. $-2(2x + 3) = -4x - 6$

7. $-5(-2x - 4) = 10x + 20$

9. $-3(x + 6) = -3x - 18$

11. $-4(-x - 6) = 4x + 24$

II. B.

1. $12 + 6x = 3(4 + 2x)$

3. $-6 - 6x = -3(2 + 2x)$

5. $-18 - 12x = -6(3 + 2x)$

7. $24 + 64x = 8(3 + 8x)$

9. $-5x - 35 = -5(x + 7)$

11. $-60x + 35 = -5(12x - 7)$

III. A.

1. $-4x - \frac{4}{9}$

3. $-13x - 3$

5. $\frac{13x}{3}$

7. $-27x - 7$

9. $-4x - 25$

11. $50x + \frac{1}{4}$

Topic 2

Two-Step Equations and Inequalities

I. A.

1. Let p represent the number of pins Eva has.
$2p + 34 = 82$
$p = 24$
Eva has 24 pins and Dulcina has 58 pins.

3. Let w represent the number of pounds Rico weighs.
$2w + 35 = 49$
$w = 7$
Rico weighs 7 pounds and Tripp weighs 42 pounds.

5. Let g represent the number of pounds of grapes Anna bought.
$4g + 2 = 14$
$g = 3$
Anna bought 3 pounds of grapes, 5 pounds of apples, and 6 pounds of bananas.

7. Let p represent the population of the Lake Section.
$3p + 188 = 4298$
$p = 1370$
The population of the Lake Section is 1370 and the population of the Hill Section is 2928.

9. Let t represent the amount the third-place seller will receive.
$4t + 24 = 104$
$t = 20$
The third-place seller will receive $20, the second-place seller will receive $28, and the first-place seller will receive $56.

11. Let t represent the number of tickets won by the friend who won fewer tickets.
$2t + 130 = 800$
$t = 335$
One friend won 335 tickets and the other won 465 tickets.

13. Let d represent the number of laps Daniel swam.
$5d + 125 = 1875$
$d = 350$
Daniel swam 350 laps, Hannah swam 700 laps, and Cameron swam 825 laps.

15. Let g represent the acres of grassy areas.
$2g + 482 = 644$
$g = 81$
There are 81 acres of grassy areas and 563 acres of woods.

PAGE 145

I. B.

1. $x = 6$
3. $d = \frac{9}{2}$
5. $w = 7.7$
7. $m = -\frac{5}{3}$
9. $c = 3\frac{1}{3}$
11. $n = -1\frac{1}{4}$

I. C.

1. $x = -3$
3. $m = -26$
5. $a = -8$
7. $s = -2$
9. $c = -\frac{1}{3}$
11. $p = -60$

II. A.

1. Yes
3. No
5. No
7. No
9. Yes
11. No

II. B.

1. $z = 3$
3. $w = -2$
5. $s = 0$
7. $b = -4$
9. $y = -14$
11. $c = -8$
13. $k = -30$
15. $y = -5$
17. $g = -2$
19. $t = -9$
21. $m = 2$
23. $x = -\frac{1}{2}$

II. C.

1. $y = \frac{5}{2}$
3. $w = -4$
5. $w = \frac{1}{5}$
7. $w = \frac{1}{3}$
9. $y = -5$
11. $w = 70$

II. D.

1. $t = \frac{d}{r}$
3. $d = 2Q - c$
5. $S = \frac{360A}{\pi r^2}$

III. A.

1.

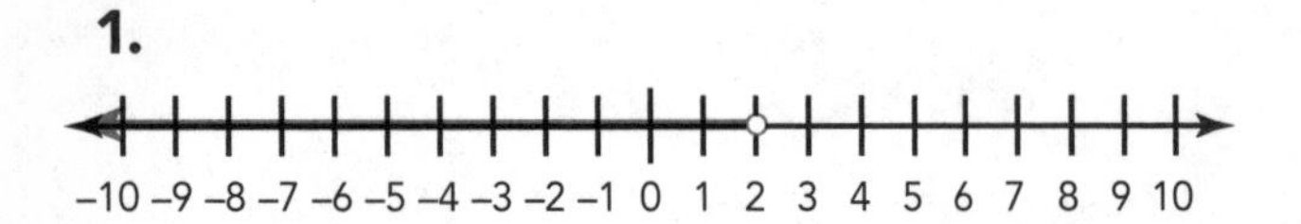

3.

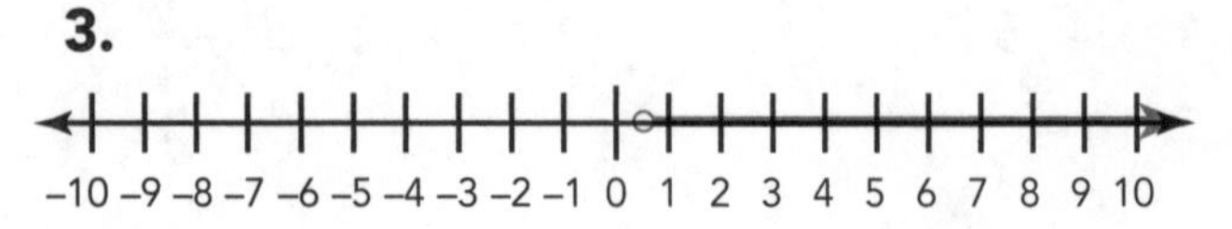

5.

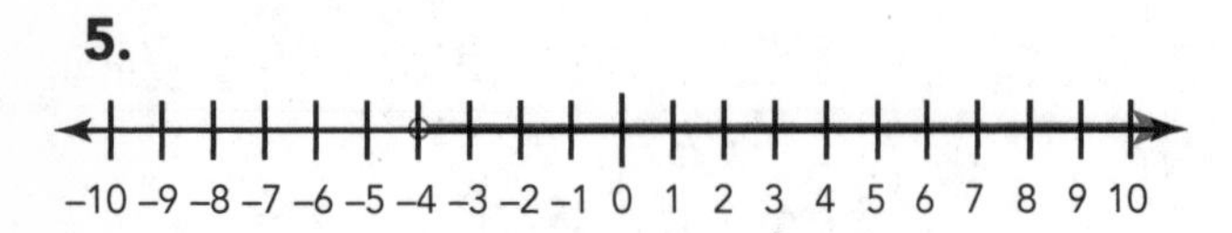

7.

9.

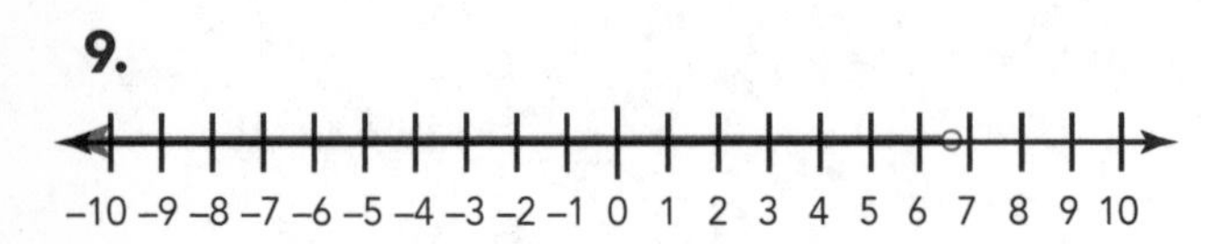

III. B.

1. $x \leq 17$

3. $x > -4$

5. $7 > x$

7. $x < -7$

9. $x \geq 13$

11. $-5 < x$

Topic 3

Multiple Representations of Equations

I. A.

1. The independent quantity is the time in seconds. The dependent quantity is the distance in meters.

3. The independent quantity is the number of members. The dependent quantity is the amount in dollars made by the club.

5. The independent quantity is the time in seconds. The dependent quantity is the distance in meters compared to the starting line.

7. The independent quantity is the time in minutes. The dependent quantity is the distance descended in feet.

9. The independent quantity is the number of miles per hour above the speed limit Francis was driving. The dependent quantity is the amount of the fine in dollars.

11. The independent quantity is the number of nail pens Alyssa buys. The dependent quantity is the amount in dollars that Alyssa pays.

I. B.

1. Santo can buy exactly 15 roses.

3. The length of each of the other two sides of the pen is exactly 10.5 yards.

5. Cameron has been painting for 12 years.

7. It has been 14 days.

9. There were 4 additional cubes.

11. It takes 10 seconds for your friend to catch up to you.

I. C.

1. Arthur can plant less than 8 plots of equal size for vegetables.

3. The principal needs to rent at least 3 buses.

5. Seiki should spend more than $6\frac{2}{3}$ minutes on each cardio machine.

7. Ms. Chu should allow more than 29 minutes for each ensemble.

9. The Pandas made less than 6 field goals.

11. Faith can package at most 5 tacos in each lunch pail.

II. A.

1.

Number of Pages	Total Cost (dollars)
2	2
10	6
15	8.50
18	10

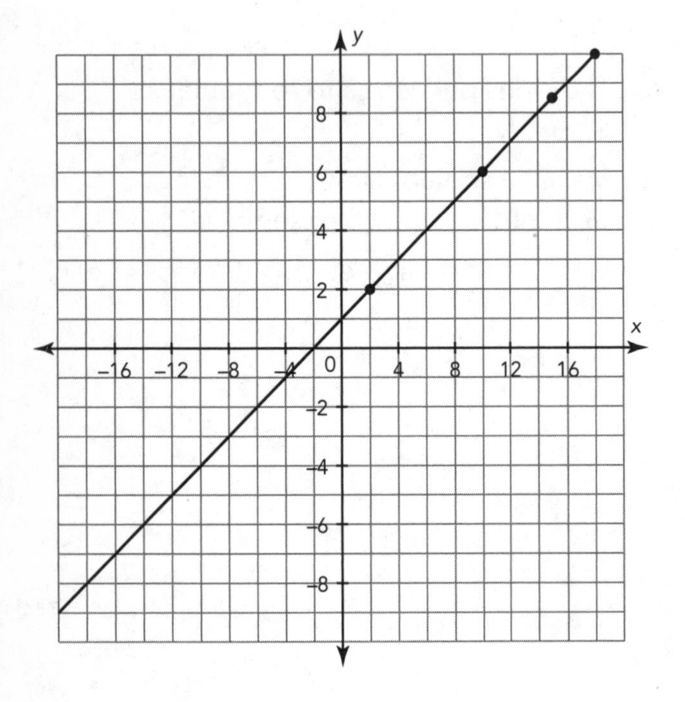

$y = 0.5x + 1$

a. 13 pages

b. $26

3.

Number of Pecks	Total Cost (dollars)
1	5
3	11
4	14
6	20

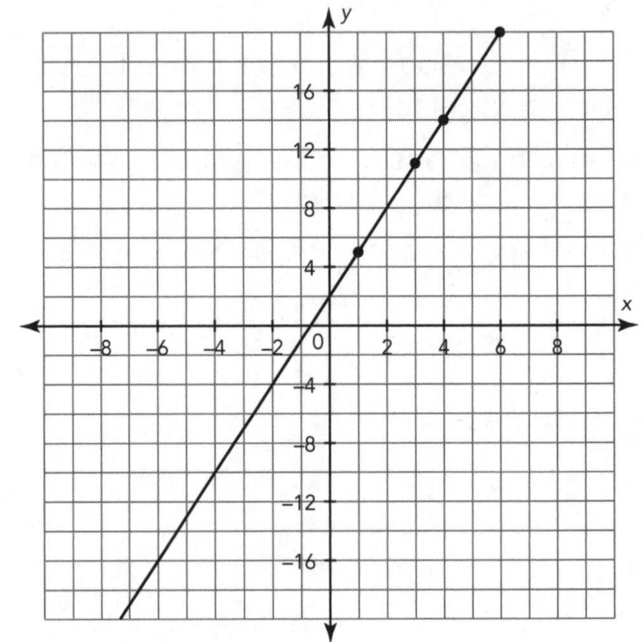

$y = 5 + 3(x - 1)$ or $y = 2 + 3x$

a. $35

b. 5 pecks

5.

Number of Balloons	Total Cost (dollars)
6	18
7	20
8	22
10	26

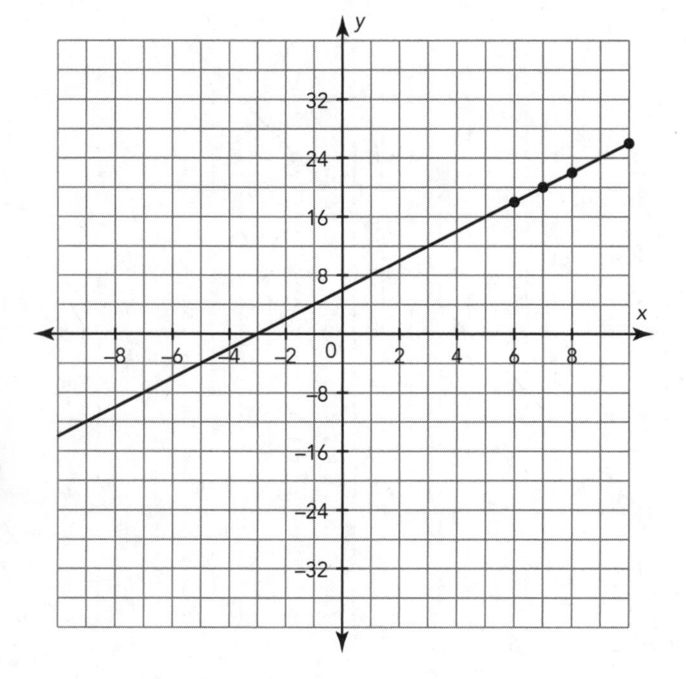

$y = 18 + 2(x - 6)$ or $y = 6 + 2x$

a. $38

b. 22 balloons

7.

Time (seconds)	Depth (meters)
8	–2
30	–7.5
37	–9.25
40	–10

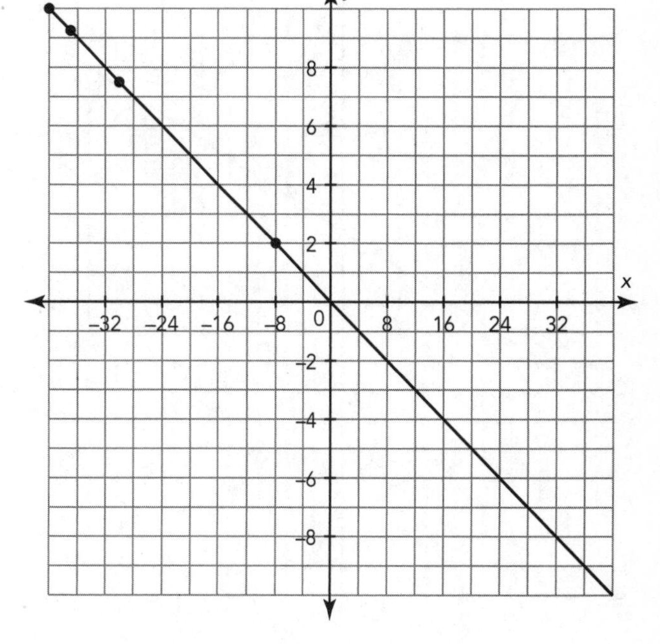

$y = -0.25x$

a. –6 meters

b. 200 seconds

9.

Time (seconds)	Height (meters)
0	50
2	75
6	125
9	162.5

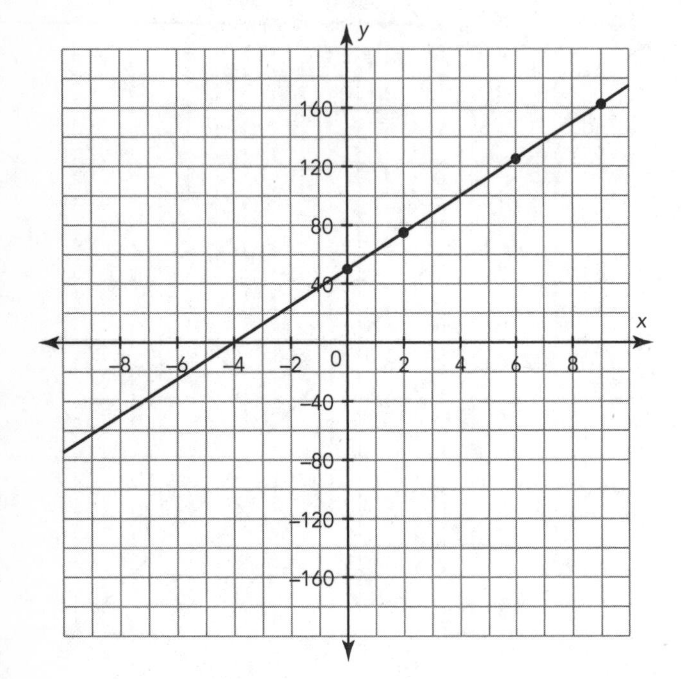

$y = 50 + 12.5x$

a. 4 seconds

b. 237.5 meters

11.

Time (months)	Total Cost (dollars)
–1	120
0	160
1	200
2	240

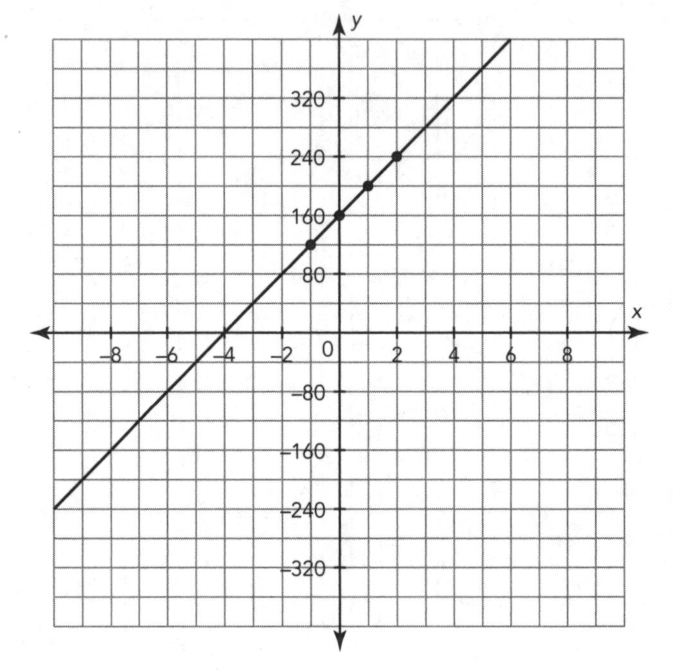

$y = 160 + 40x$

a. –1.5, or 1.5 months ago

b. $40

III. A.

1. $t = 169.90 + 15.99\ (g - 10)$

3. $t = 330 + 11.5\ (s - 20)$

5. $h = 4 + 3w$

III. B.

1. 15 meters per second

3. −14 meters per minute

5. −18.5 meters per minute

MODULE 4

Topic 1

Introduction to Probability

I. A.

1. 0

3. 1

5. 1

I. B.

1. $\frac{1}{5}$

3. $\frac{2}{5}$

5. 0

I. C.

1. $\frac{8}{46} = \frac{4}{23}$

3. $\frac{8}{46} = \frac{4}{23}$

5. $\frac{19}{46}$

7. $\frac{27}{46}$

II. A.

1.

Outcome	1	2	3	4	5	6	7	8	9	10
Probability	0.1	0.1	0.1	0.1	0.1	0.1	0.1	0.1	0.1	0.1

uniform probability model

3.

Outcome	1	2	3	4	5	6	7	8
Probability	$\frac{1}{8}$	$\frac{1}{8}$	$\frac{1}{8}$	$\frac{1}{8}$	$\frac{1}{8}$	$\frac{1}{8}$	$\frac{1}{8}$	$\frac{1}{8}$

uniform probability model

5.

Outcome	Blue	Red	Yellow
Probability	$\frac{3}{8}$	$\frac{3}{8}$	$\frac{1}{4}$

non-uniform probability model

7.

Outcome	Sun.	Mon.	Tue.	Wed.	Thur.	Fri.y	Sat.
Probability	$\frac{1}{7}$	$\frac{1}{7}$	$\frac{1}{7}$	$\frac{1}{7}$	$\frac{1}{7}$	$\frac{1}{7}$	$\frac{1}{7}$

uniform probability model

9.

Outcome	HH	HT	TH	TT
Probability	$\frac{1}{4}$	$\frac{1}{4}$	$\frac{1}{4}$	$\frac{1}{4}$

uniform probability model

11.

Outcome	Red	Blue	Green	Yellow	Purple
Probability	$\frac{1}{5}$	$\frac{1}{5}$	$\frac{1}{5}$	$\frac{1}{5}$	$\frac{1}{5}$

uniform probability model

III. A.

1.

Result	Tally	Total
Heads	𝍸 III	8
Tails	𝍸 𝍸 II	12
		20

$P(\text{tails}) = \frac{12}{20} = 60$

3.

Result	Tally	Total
White	𝍸 𝍸 II	12
Brown	III	3
		15

$P(\text{brown}) = \frac{3}{15} = \frac{1}{5} = 20$

5.

Result	Tally	Total
Dime	𝍸 𝍸 II	12
Nickel	𝍸 IIII	9
Penny	IIII	4
		25

$P(\text{nickel}) = \frac{9}{25} = 36$

Topic 2

Compound Probability

I. A.

1. $P(\text{A or B}) = \frac{2}{6}$ or $\frac{1}{3}$

3. $P(\text{not C}) = \frac{5}{6}$

5. $P(\text{D, E, or F}) = \frac{3}{6}$ or $\frac{1}{2}$

I. B.

1. $P(\text{polygon}) = \frac{5}{6}$

3. $P(\text{triangle or circle}) = \frac{3}{6}$ or $\frac{1}{2}$

5. $P(\text{more than four sides}) = \frac{1}{6}$

I. C.

1. $P(\text{even and even}) = \frac{6}{30}$ or $\frac{1}{5}$

3. $P(\text{spin less than 4 or roll less than 4}) = \frac{24}{30}$ or $\frac{4}{5}$

5. $P(\text{spin 5 or roll 5}) = \frac{10}{30}$ or $\frac{1}{3}$

I. D.

1. $P(\text{unique colors}) = \frac{10}{12}$ or $\frac{5}{6}$

3. $P(\text{blue first or blue second}) = \frac{6}{12}$ or $\frac{1}{2}$

5. $P(\text{red first or yellow second}) = \frac{6}{12}$ or $\frac{1}{2}$

Topic 3

Drawing Inferences

I. A.

1. sample

3. sample

5. census

I. B.

1. statistic

3. statistic

5. parameter

II. A.

1. The sample is not random because team members whose last names start with consonants have no chance of being selected.
3. The sample is random because each team member has an equal chance of being selected.
5. The sample is not random because it only focuses on the early customers whose eating habits may be different from later customers.

II. B.

1. The first four random student numbers are 14, 24, 22, and 19.
3. The names of the students are Noah, Aki, and Sherwin.
5. The names of the students are Jada and Wei.

III. A.

1. Set 1: mean = 6.8
   MAD = 3.04

   Set 2: mean = 14.4
   MAD = 10.24

   The difference in the means is 7.6, which falls between the mean absolute deviation of Set 1 and Set 2.
3. Set 1: mean = 64.6
   MAD = 8.56

   Set 2: mean = 45.4
   MAD = 26.72

   The difference in the means is 19.1, which falls between the mean absolute deviation of Set 1 and Set 2.
5. Mocha: mean = 32
   MAD = 10.4

   Cinnamon: mean = 83
   MAD = 7.6

   The difference in the means is 51 which is greater than the mean absolute deviation of both sets.

PAGE 155

IV. A.

1. Set 1: median = 54
IQR = 56

Set 2: median = 52
IQR = 52.5

3. Set 1: median = 50
IQR = 54

Set 2: median = 63
IQR = 79

5. Answers may vary.
Top plot: median = 100
IQR = 110

Bottom plot: median = 100
IQR = 40

MODULE 5

Topic 1

Angles and Triangles

I. A.

1. supplementary angles

3. supplementary angles

5. vertical angles

I. B.

1. none of these

3. vertical angles

5. complementary angles

II. A.

1. $x = 57.5$

3. $x = 143$

5. $x = 54$

III. A.

1. Yes

3. No

5. No

7. Yes

9. No

11. No

Topic 2

Three-Dimensional Figures

I. A.

1. 27.5 cubic inches

3. 184 cubic feet

5. 3658.67 cubic millimeters

II. A.

1. 132 square inches

3. 1498 square meters

5. 185,625 square feet

II. B.

1. 7 feet

3. 4.4 centimeters

5. 14.01 centimeters